Parenting with Confidence

Chap Bettis

Author of *The Disciple-Making Parent*

Parenting *with* Confidence

Biblical Truth in a Chaotic World

DIAMOND HILL PUBLISHING

PARENTING WITH CONFIDENCE: Biblical Truth in a Chaotic World
Copyright © 2022 by Chap Bettis.
Diamond Hill Publishing
All rights reserved.
ISBN-13: 978-0-9990410-5-5

Visit **ParentingwithConfidenceStudy.com**
to access the accompanying videos.

TABLE OF CONTENTS

Lesson 1

Understanding How the World Influences Us 1

   Parents, Understand How The World Influences You 3

Lesson 2

Understanding the Big Themes of Scripture **9**

   Parents, Understand Who Your Child Is 10

   Parents, Understand Who You Are 11

   Parents, Be Clear on Where You are Going 12

   Parents, Be Clear on What a Family Is 12

   Parents, Let Authority and Affection Be Your Bedrocks 16

   Parents, Strive to Create a Strong Family Identity 18

   Parents, Build Family Affection with Meals 20

   Parents, Use Mealtime to Build Each Other Up 23

   Parents, Build Family Affection at Bedtime 24

   Parents, Use Vacations and Family Trips to Build Family Unity . .25

   Parents, Teach Your Children to Honor Their Grandparents . . 27

Lesson 3

Understanding What God Commands **31**

   Parents, Know and Believe What God Says to Your Child 32

   Parents, Teach and Train for First-Time Obedience 34

   Parents, Know and Believe What God Says to You 35

   Parents, Understand the Funnel Principle 36

   Parents, Speak with Verbal Authority 40

   Parents, "OK?" is Not Ok 42

   Parents, Train Your Children to Be Polite 44

Lesson 4

Understanding Training and Instruction 47

Parents, Know Your Tools, How to Use Them, and How

They Change Over Time 48

Parents, Use Action More Than Words for Young Children . . .49

Parents, Understand the Biblical Pattern of Change:

Putting Off and Putting On 50

Parents, Train, Train, and Retrain. 50

Parents, Rest on the Three-Legged Stool 51

Parents, Cast a Vision for the Positive 52

Parents, Have a Plan and Keep Track of Correction

Using a Character Chart 53

Parents, For Older Children, Include the Heart on

The Character Chart 55

Parents, Make Sure the Shepherds are Meeting

on a "Coffee Date". 56

Parents, Think about How Parenting Changes Over the Years . .60

Parents, Give Them Grace by Giving Them the Law 62

Lesson 5

Understanding the Need for Habits, Routine, Rules,

and Self-Discipline 65

Parents, Structure the Environment 66

Parents, Calm the Chaos and Don't Be a Bedraggled Parent . . .67

Parents, Ask Questions to Remind Your Children about

Family Rules 70

Parents, Think about Your Baby's First Year and Beyond 72

Parents, Have a Media Plan and Monitor Their Media. 75

Parents, Know How Routines Will Help You Thrive 78

Lesson 6

Understanding Correction, Consequences, Chastisement, and Rewards **85**

    Parents, Use Correction, Consequences, Chastisement, and Rewards 86

    Parents, Prayerfully Consider Using Chastisement. 89

    Parents, Understand Miscellaneous Principles for Obedience 91

    Parents, Think About Rewards 92

    Parents, Consistency is Vital. Be Consistent, Even When You Don't Feel like it 93

    Parents, Realize That, Out of Love, God Trains Us with Things that are Unpleasant 93

    Parents, Parent By Faith Not Fear 93

    Parents, Understand an Abbreviated Plan for Child-Rearing . . .96

    Dad, Take the Lead in Discipline. Mom, Do Your Part 98

    Parents, Hand Out Consequences Consistently 100

    Parents, Know How to Handle Parenting Disagreements Among Yourselves. 102

    Parents, Think About How to Handle Grandparents Who Disagree With You. 104

    Parents, Know How to Overcome Your Anger 106

Lesson 7

Understanding How to Get Started **111**

    Parents, Don't Be Discouraged, Think About Getting Started. . 112

About the Author

Chap Bettis is the author of *The Disciple-Making Parent: Raising Your Children to Love and Follow Jesus Christ*. Since its release, *The Disciple-Making Parent* has quickly become the premier resource for helping families and churches pass the gospel to their children. It has been endorsed by a growing list of Christian leaders including: Dr. Albert Mohler, Tim Challies, Dr. David Murray, Dr. Tim Lane, Dr. Wayne Mack, Marty Machowski, Jackie Kendall, and David and Sally Michael. More information is available at thedisciplemakingparent.com or on his podcast – The Disciple-Making Parent.

Chap is also a frequent conference speaker and the executive director of The Disciple-Making Parent Ministries which is devoted to helping parents train their children to love Jesus Christ. His articles have appeared on the websites of The Gospel Coalition, The Ethics and Religious Liberty Counsel, Rooted, and Crosswalk.

For the previous 25 years, he was lead pastor in a New England church plant. He and his wife Sharon have four adult children and reside in Rhode Island. He also authored *The Donut Date Journal, Evangelism for the Tongue-Tied*, and The *Fearless Apologetics Curriculum*.

When he is not ministering the Word, Chap likes cycling, skiing, reading, and checking out Providence restaurants with his wife. You can follow him on Twitter or Instagram @chapbettis or on his blog at thedisciplemakingparent.com.

Introduction and How to Use this Study

Do you feel unsure in your parenting?

Do you find yourself worried you will mess up your child? These are common and understandable feelings. But you don't have to feel that way. That's not part of God's plan for his people. I promise that you can parent by faith and not fear!

The Lord has given us a sure guide in his Word. While the Bible is not a parenting manual, it is meant to equip us to live the Christian life (2 Tim 3:16-17), and that includes parenting! The more you know God's Word, the more confident you will be. You can parent by faith and not fear.

This study will help you discover rich biblical themes, insights, and commands that will give you confidence in your parenting. You will meet each day knowing that God will give you the needed wisdom by his Spirit and his Word.

Overview of Each Lesson

The workbook is made up of seven lessons. Most lessons consist of two videos to watch, a place to take notes, and questions for discussion or personal reflection.

You can find the accompanying videos at ParentingwithConfidenceStudy.com.

Each lesson also includes other small essays related to the topic that was covered. Notice the way to understand the theme is by the highlighted sentences that start with, "Parents, . . ." This study is filled with these encouragements that summarize the video lesson or the short essays that follow.

Teaching This Study

Although you can find benefit from completing this material by yourself, studying and discussing it with others will create the most benefit. It is perfect for a small group study.

An easy way to use the material is for 6-7 week small group study. If you are running short on time, some have found it helpful to simply present a summary of Lesson 5 on routines. In addition, you might want to devote extra time to Lesson 6, which deals with discipline and rewards.

Intended Audience

This study is targeted for followers of Jesus Christ - those who have repented of their sins and trusted in his full atonement on the cross. However, if that is not you for some reason, you will still be helped by the teaching in this material.

In addition, while the study is primarily aimed at parents of younger children, I think parents of all aged children could benefit by being reminded of biblical principles that apply to all parents. Our core convictions can become fuzzy after years of parenting. In addition, I believe that all those who are actively shepherding children, such as grandparents and children's ministry workers, could also benefit from the material.

Raising Children in Community

This study assumes that you are involved in a healthy local church. My wife and I owe a debt of gratitude to the many families with whom we raised our children. We were, and still are, able to be honest about the challenges of raising the children God has given us. The community, including the older saints, was invaluable. Make sure you are inviting input from others.

Connect with Us

Finally, I would love to connect with you. Sign up for our weekly email at thedisciplemakingparent.com. Every Friday I send out thoughts and suggested articles about parenting. In addition, connect with us on social media and our podcast for smaller, bitesized encouragement.

I am praying the Lord's blessing on your study. If you are ready and willing to grow in your understanding, then let's get started. You can parent with confidence!

Chap Bettis

Visit **ParentingwithConfidenceStudy.com**
to access the accompanying videos.

Understanding How the World Influences Us

LECTURE NOTES

▶ **LESSON 1 - VIDEO A: INTRODUCTION**

What We are Hoping to Accomplish

You will learn this material in a like-minded community.

This will help a husband and wife be unified.

You will have humility, intentional teachability.

An Overview
1. How the World Presses/Influences Us

2. Biblical Themes

3. God Speaks to Children and Parents

4. Wisdom Applications

5. The Study Bible Analogy

A Disclaimer about Families with Foster or Special Needs Children

A Disclaimer about the Author's Family

Your Opportunity as a Parent to Learn about Your Heavenly Father

Parents, Know How The World Influences You

What does the culture tell us about good parenting?

Finish the sentence,

"A good parent will do _____ for his/her child."

The Air We Breathe/Cultural Messages that Influence Us

1. Children are the _____ of our universe.

2. Children are naturally _____ _____

    a. Therefore, we should never say _____ .

    b. Children can't be expected to _____ .

3. Children have _____ self-esteem.

The most common fear – "If I don't do it right, I will _____ my child."

Remember – Rousseau gave away his children!

4. Children need lots of _____ .

5. Two more in the Christian community.

   a. All of parenting needs to be _____ centered.

   b. All physical _____ is wrong.

NOTES

NOTES

REFLECTION QUESTIONS

Use the following questions to guide your discussion.

1. What challenges are you currently facing in your parenting? What are you hoping to take away from this investment of time?

2. If you are married, what tensions are there over childrearing? For example, he is strict and she is permissive or the other way around. Write these down honestly so that we can talk about them.

3. Which cultural influences are affecting you most? (For example, social media, parenting books, peers, blogs, fear of others judgment, your own fears.)

Understanding The Big Themes of Scripture

LECTURE NOTES

Parents, Understand Who Your Child Is

What child is this?

1. Your child is an eternal _____ .

2. Your child is an image bearer.

3. Your child is a _____ personality.

    But...personality is not destiny.

4. Your child is a trust.

5. Your child is an _____ to your family.

6. Your child is _____.

7. Your child is uneducated.

8. Your child needs the Savior and the gospel.

Parents, Understand Who You Are

Who am I?

1. You are an agent/bearer of God's _____.

2. You are a _____ child.

3. You are a sinning _____.

4. You are a Christian with your _____ in Christ.

5. You are a married person (plus a word to single parents).

6. You are a Christian called to live out gospel _____.

7. You are _____ God, Jesus Christ, or the Holy Spirit.

Parents, Be Clear on Where You are Going

What is the North Star that we are aiming at?

An adult _____ of Jesus Christ.

Heaven or Harvard?

What is best? The _____ .

> " Your family is meant to be a God-glorifying, disciple-making unit."

Parents, Be Clear on What a Family Is

1. You are a family.

2. You are a reflection of the _____.

3. As such, you are to be full of affection and _____.

See the short essays on the following pages:
- *Parents, Let Authority and Affection be Your Bedrocks*
- *Parents, Strive to Create a Strong Family Identity*
- *Parents, Build Family Affection with Meals*
- *Parents, Use Mealtime to Build Each Other Up*
- *Parents, Build Family Affection at Bedtime*
- *Parents, Use Vacations and Family Trips to Build Family Unity*
- *Parents, Teach Your Children to Honor Their Grandparents*

For deeper understanding of these themes check out
The Disciple-Making Parent at: **thedisciplemakingparent.com**

NOTES

NOTES

PARENTING WITH CONFIDENCE

REFLECTION QUESTIONS

Use the following questions to guide your discussion.

1. Which of the biblical truths about your children was most significant? Why?

2. Which of the biblical truths about you as a parent was most significant? Why?

3. Do you tend to emphasize authority or affection in your parenting?

4. Look over the extra essays. Which was most helpful? Why?

ESSAYS

Parents, Let Authority and Affection Be Your Bedrocks

"Parenting is about authority and affection."

I find myself coming back to this phrase again and again as I seek to help younger parents.

This insight is not original with me. Nor is it even originally intended for human parents. The great Charles Spurgeon had this to say about our heavenly Father in his devotional, *Morning and Evening*:

> God's people are doubly His children, they are His offspring by creation, and they are His sons by adoption in Christ. Hence they are privileged to call Him, "Our Father which art in heaven." Father! Oh, what precious word is that.

> Here is authority: "If I be a Father, where is mine honor?" If ye be sons, where is your obedience? Here is affection mingled with authority; an authority which does not provoke rebellion; an obedience demanded which is most cheerfully rendered-which would not be withheld even if it might.

If our heavenly Father mingles affection and authority, how much more should earthly parents seek to imitate him?

Authority

As parents, God has given us real authority to exercise for the good of our children. God commands our children to honor us and to obey our words. This is for their benefit, not ours. As Ephesians 6:3 states, we do this training so that it may go well with them. When we teach our children to place themselves under our authority, we are training the same spiritual muscle that will later more easily place itself under our heavenly Father.

While obedience cannot regenerate the heart, it can shape it in a positive way. J.C. Ryle observed, "You must not wonder that men refuse to obey their Father which is in heaven, if you allow them, when children, to disobey, their father who is upon earth."

God calls us to lovingly exercise our authority. We should feel comfortable giving commands, direction, and wisdom to our children. We should also feel comfortable training their character by bringing consequences after the inevitable disobedience. If we don't train them to obey, we are training them to disobey.

Affection

In addition to exercising authority, we must also be comfortable expressing affection. God doesn't merely love us with a detached, objective love. We are told the Father's love is an affectionate, tender love (Zephaniah 3:17). It is a warm and intimate love. Isn't this affection what also made Jesus so attractive to sinners?

We exemplify our heavenly Father when we have a warmhearted, emotionally connected relationship with our children. When we smile, hug, and talk with them, we are showing them the love of the Father. When we listen to and laugh with them, we are displaying the affectionate care of the Father.

Boundaries and Warmth

Christian Smith, who has written about religious parents passing along their values, records these exact components in different words. He writes:

> Though the influence of parenting style is known to vary somewhat by race and ethnicity, it is broadly true that the religious parents who most successfully raise religious children tend to exhibit an "authoritative" parenting style. Such parents combine two crucial traits. First, they consistently hold their children to clear and demanding expectations, standards, and boundaries in all areas of life. Second, they relate to their children with an abundance of warmth, support, and expressive care. It is not hard to see why this parenting style works best for raising religious children. The combination of clear expectations and affective warmth is powerful in children's developmental formation.[1]

Affection and authority are key characteristics of gospel parents. Really, these are key components of any gospel leadership. However, for most parents, one of these will come naturally while the other will feel more difficult. It will take effort to grow in both expressions of care for your children.

In addition, we must fight against the pressure of our current culture. Authority is now suspect. Parents around us are fearful of messing up their children with correction. But as we have seen above, it is loving to have a home with expectations, boundaries, and consequences. I have said to young parents on many occasions, "When it comes to affection and authority, this generation is nailing the affection part of parenting but is missing the authority part."

Parents, you have been given the privilege of influencing an eternal soul. We are to imitate our heavenly Father as we care for our children. "Affection mingled with authority" should be our two great bedrocks as we build our own household and the household of God.

1. www.firstthings.com/article/2021/05/keeping-the-faith

Parents, Strive to Create a Strong Family Identity

Our God is corporate. He is a Tri-unity. Three different persons but living as a unity. One God.

For those of us in the West, it is easy to see our family as a collection of individuals who live under the same roof. We receive benefit from this arrangement, but often do not see the family as a unit.

In the case of a marriage ceremony, two individuals walk into the ceremony single. Then right before our eyes we see something new created – a marriage.

Similarly, if God wills, this family will create new life, who will be added to the family. Part of our job as parents is to help children overcome their natural selfishness of thinking the family is about them.

We want them to have an all-for-one and a one-for-all attitude. In the midst of the rough and tumble of daily growing up, God has sovereignly placed these individuals as parents, brother and sisters.

How can we create that family affection? There are a number of ways.

1. Urge an all-for-one and one-for-all attitude where the children appropriately serve, sympathize, and pitch in to build up the family.

2. Eat meals together regularly. As the following article shows, meals bind our hearts together.

3. Create family memories and family traditions. Use family vacations and holidays to build warmth and connection. Many times we go through the motions on these things without realizing the *why* of what we are doing.

4. Serve together. Serve each other. Serve others together. Be outward focused servants of Christ. Resist child-centered self-indulgence. Don't be self-focused worshipers of the family. Serving together builds family unity.

5. Don't allow sibling rivalry to tear the family apart. Family unity displays the Triune God to the watching world. God gives us very practical advice about unkind words and actions, asking forgiveness, and making restitution. Conflict is inevitable. Destructive conflict does not need to be.

6. Keep the marriage first. We have already talked about this in Video 2B. Children will be more affectionate as they know Mom and Dad's relationship is secure.

7. Choose outside activities wisely and carefully. Remember, they often come at the price of family togetherness. I know numerous families kept outside activities very low when their children were small so they could focus on family togetherness and character building. Later, they got their teens involved in outside activities. But it requires wisdom, because sometimes those activities can give you something to do together and build family unity.

Having a family that *generally* displays loving affection is a goal to strive after.

Parents, Build Family Affection with Meals

As I travel about, I see many good families who are not thoughtful in the area of family meals. And we are the poorer for it. In this essay, I want to argue for why you should be intentional about your family meals and offer practical tips for pulling it off.

The Power of Family Meals

Eating a meal with someone is a powerful thing. From the unspoken security of a meal eaten in peace, to the context for personal communication, eating with someone creates relationship as well as feeds from it. Researchers have long been showing us the power of a nightly family dinner.

So much so that Miriam Weinstein begins her 2005 book, *The Surprising Power of Family Meals* with these words,

> What if I told you that there was a magic bullet–something that would i mprove the quality of your daily life, your children's chances of success in the world, your family's health, our values as a society? Something that is inexpensive, simple to produce and within the reach of pretty much anyone?

Harvard professor, author, and family therapist Anne Fishel has pointed to countless studies that have shown that young children gain a higher vocabulary at the dinner table than being read to nightly. In older children, family dinners are a predictor for higher test scores than time at school, playing sports, or doing art. In teens, many studies show that regular family dinners are linked with lowering the risk of smoking, binge drinking, marijuana use, violence, school problems, eating disorders, and sexual activity. Another study of 5000 Minnesota teens found regular family dinners associated with lower rates of depression and suicidal thoughts. Meals are powerful.

The Current State of Meals

For too many families the family meal has disappeared or is in tatters. One study found that 67% of families had the TV playing during dinner. In other families, children eat before the parents arrive and leave the table before the adults are finished. Individuals eat in shifts.

Having family meals together might be the most Christian countercultural thing you can do.

I want to plead with Mom or Dad to create a family culture where meals and mealtime conversation are treasured. Although not perfect by any means, Sharon and I tried to create a culture that valued the family meal.

When our children were young, we made an effort to eat together. This meant training young children in table manners. Even when we started to be more involved in outside activities, we still tried to have regular family meals together.

We tried to have at least one meal a day where whoever was home sat down to eat together. Electronic devices were put away. We wanted to create a boundary around this mealtime.

Mealtimes provide the opportunity to teach without "teaching." It provides the opportunity to teach manners and self-control. Teaching good table manners provide life-long benefits. It allows us to build family unity. We can hear about the high and lows of the day. We can hand out "The Red Plate (see article below).

Some Practical Suggestions from Our Experience Preparation
One or more of the children would set the table. It was his or her chore. Perhaps that child would help Mom with cooking. This was a rotating chore and gave the child one on one time with mom. We were also trying to use this to cultivate a servant heart.

One child would help Mom serve. With four children two years apart, we needed all hands on deck when the children were young and when they were older.

Actively train young children in table manners. They can be trained; they don't have to throw food.

Participation
No one started eating until we all sat down. Here we were trying to teach self-control. The whole family sat down together to eat. Of course, there were exceptions such as feeding a baby in a high-chair or giving carrots for snacks. But there was no sense of giving a child his dinner before the rest of us.

We expected proper manners (within their ability of course). This includes not talking with your mouth full.

We expected good and fun conversation. Dad or Mom took the lead in talking. Sometimes we would talk with each other while the children listened while other times each would report to Dad about the day's activities. Sometimes devotions would start in the middle. If we had a guest over, we expected them to listen to the guest or ask a question we had given them earlier.

When the children were younger, we would work on the wiggles by putting chocolate chips in front of their plate as rewards. If they had some minor infraction, one would get taken away. The goal, of course, was to have all at the end of the night – which were then doubled.

Often, we would have family devotions over dessert. But to have dessert, we had to do a tiny clean up and get a little dessert on the table. If we had dessert, we waited until the server joined us. That usually meant that we looked at our dessert for 30 seconds until Mom sat down. When she took "the official bite" the rest of us would eat. Again, we were trying to teach self-control and consideration. And the kids had fun waiting for Mom to take...drum roll...*the official bite.*

In addition, dessert (or chocolate chips) was a reward for eating what was on your plate. If it wasn't finished it came out for lunch the next day. There was also no extending dinner. If they were not done when the rest of us were done, then the food got put away.

Do we need to say it – Put down the phone – Dad, Mom, children. Our rule, in the day of the answering machine, was that we never answered the phone. This dinner time was so small and so valuable, the other phone call could be returned.

Post-Dinner
For family devotions, the Bibles were nearby as were little hand toys if we were going to be sitting at the table awhile.

Finally, to get down, they had to ask if they could be excused. Again, we wanted to teach self-control and submission to our authority.

One or two were assigned to clean up. Often it was Dad and one of the children.

Do You Believe in the Power of Family Meals?
Can this be modified? Yes, of course. But as you can see, dinner was a priority and an event. It bound our hearts together, allowed them to develop broad taste buds, and developed their conversational skills.

Did we have some issues? Yes, of course. But overall, God honored this routine. But it starts with having a high view of the mealtime event. It continues with the idea that children can be trained in self-control (waiting on food, sitting at the dinner table, asking to get down). It resonates because we also want to teach skills like listening to each other and celebrating each other's victories and consoling each other. We wanted to create an all-for-one and one-for-all attitude.

Family meals are a sign and seal of our family unity. They powerfully bind hearts together. We underestimate them to our own detriment. Imagine the blessing on the relationships in your family as you eat thousands of meals together over the years.

Parents, Use Mealtime to Build Each Other Up

Life can be discouraging for our children. It can seem like we are always correcting them. Things don't always go their way. In addition, family squabbling can also deflate the atmosphere in our homes. What if I told you of one simple trick to change the tone of your house? Sharon and I practiced this consistently around our family dinners and it often provided a much-needed boost.

It is the tradition of The Red Plate.

As the leaders of our home, we have the power to make it an encouraging place or a discouraging place. In the late 1980's, when I was a computer programmer, our team had – "The Pumpkin." The Pumpkin was a small ceramic pumpkin that sat in the cubicle of the last person who had messed up. Even though it was given out in fun, it still sent a message. So when a more encouraging manager took over our team, The Pumpkin was the first thing to go in the trash.

Giving The Pumpkin or The Red Plate?
Some of us parent with The Pumpkin in mind – thinking about and reminding our children of the day's failures. While there is a place for correcting the negative, how much better to catch our children doing something right. And so our family copied the tradition of The Red Plate.

Around the time we were raising our children, many families were buying a red plate that said, "You are special." Liking the idea but not wanting to spend the money, we bought our own regular red plate and bowl. The red plate came out at special times to celebrate a family member.

Why is The Red Plate Powerful?
1. **It gives you the power to highlight something that might go unnoticed**. We did use the plate for something that we all celebrate – like birthdays. But more often, we used it to highlight one child who had been especially loving or kind or studied hard. Rather than rewarding outcomes, we tried to reward godly character.

2. **It contributes a positive tone to your house**. Rather than focusing on correction, it moved our focus to affirmation. We were trying to be a happy family, catching others doing something right.

3. **It teaches your other children to rejoice with those that rejoice.** The Red Plate turned the attention to one special family member and created a sense of family identity. We wanted the other children to have an "all-for-one and one-for-all mentality. The Red Plate was a way to actively train this attitude.

4. **It gives direction to your dinner time discussions.** The Red Plate given by Mom allows the whole family to report to Dad what the recipient did. And Dad should be the chief affirmation officer. This gives him a chance for the whole family to hear his praise. (And it is really encouraging when Mom gives it to Dad or Dad gives it to Mom!)So buy your own red plate and start celebrating each other. You will only be sorry you did not start earlier.

Parents, Build Family Affection at Bedtime

Bedtimes also have the potential to be powerful relational and spiritual times. Children's hearts are more open. It is often a tender time to reflect on the day.

Just as with the previous essay, don't think of this essay as demanding law. There were nights I was so tired I practically threw my children into bed trusting that we would reconnect in the morning when I wasn't exhausted.

But bedtime was a connection time that either my wife or I wanted to strive for.

Here are some principles you might follow.

1. You determine bedtime and how much sleep your children need based on age, circumstances, and your personal knowledge of them.

2. Don't just send kids to bed, put them to bed. Read to them, tuck them in, talk with them, listen to them, pray with them, tell them you love them, etc. This is a great time to read a Bible story for the younger ones. Or have the older ones read a devotional book.

3. As you tuck them in, master the art of open-ended questions. "What was the high and low of the day?" "Is there anything about today that is troubling you?" "Is there anything bothering your conscience that you want to tell me about?"

4. Train the young ones not to get out of bed. We rewarded with music and storytapes. This served a double duty. We were occupying them and teaching them when they could not go to sleep. If one had a late nap, they might not be sleepy, but Mom and Dad needed a break! So bedtime stayed the same with something to occupy them. This is an important issue to train for. Use the Character Chart (in Lesson 4) if necessary.

5. No electronics/TVs in the bedroom in the evening. Keep them downstairs or in a common area. Use something else for an alarm clock. There is nothing good your teen will miss by not being online at night and there is plenty of bad he will miss. Studies show that screens are affecting children's sleep.

6. Remember, for teens, the most profitable discussions often happen after bedtimes... Your bedtime! Be ready for it. And try and make the sacrifice.

Parents, Use Vacations and Family Trips to Build Family Unity

Family trips, also known as vacations, are not a break from intentional parenting but rather a deliberate tool in intentional parenting. However, for some families, while vacations promise much, they often highlight our own selfishness and fail to deliver. Our family certainly had its share of meltdowns on vacation, but the following principles might be helpful to you.

1. Remember a vacation and a family trip are two different things. I can't remember where I heard this, but it is key to managing my expectations. When you are taking young children along you are not going on vacation; you are going on a family trip. If I have expectations of complete rest on a trip with children, I will become upset and angry. No, a family trip requires lots of service on my part. I may have moments of vacation. Or maybe my wife and I will take some time off later. But when the children are young, family trips require work.

2. Family trips are a powerful opportunity to build family identity and family memories. For many years, we drove our young children down to Alabama to visit their grandparents. That 22-hour, 2-day trip was exhausting. In the days before DVDs, we had to strategize about keeping them occupied (book time, game time, story time, etc.). But when we talk about those trips now, our children have fond memories. Why? Our family was together having fun. That time in the car, even with the diaper explosions, was a great help in building family identity.

We are not just six individuals living under the same roof. The Lord has put us together as a family. Time away can help reinforce this truth.

3. Family trips offer everyone a chance to develop a heart of service. To paraphrase Augustine, sin causes us to curve in on ourselves. And family trips magnify that curve. However, the unique challenges also give us a chance to grow in serving others. In addition, it is a chance to train our children in service as well. Older children can help with younger children. Everyone can help serve Mom (or Dad). We all can show honor to our grandparents. The natural self-centeredness I feel, my children feel also. We will need to fight that by the power of the Spirit.

4. Family trips offer a chance to learn about the larger body of Christ. We tried to make it a habit to go to church on family trips. Visiting churches in different parts of the country exposed our children to other believers. Did they complain sometimes? Of course. But it gave them a richer perspective and was teaching our own values without trying.

5. Family trips need margin to succeed. How many times did I have to learn this the hard way? The bigger the ship, the more margin it takes. Something always goes wrong. I need to remember that I love my family by making sure we have plenty of margin. In addition to planning activities, unhurried conversations with my children were also valuable. And those only happened because we had margin.

6. Family trips give us a chance to express praise and thankfulness. No matter where we go or don't go, having time off is an expression of God's kindness. There are plenty of impoverished families around the world who cannot even think of taking time off. No matter what goes wrong (and it will), my heart of praise and thankfulness is key. Family times together give us a chance to praise our Creator for his creation. And they give us a chance to deliberately express thankfulness for each in the family.

Family trips are not a break from discipleship. Rather, they are another God-given opportunity to love on your own family and develop your own Christlikeness. To coin a phrase – Don't waste your family trip!

Parents, Teach Your Children to Honor Their Grandparents

Family relationships are tricky. Sin affects everything including our families. And that certainly applies to our extended family. Grandparents can be a blessing, require some tricky navigation, or be a constant challenge.

But more often what I worry about is how our cultural child-centeredness influences how families view grandparents. The very nature of sin causes all of us to curve in on ourselves. As a result, I wonder if God's call to honor those who are older, especially grandparents, has fallen on hard times. Are we asking grandparents to honor the grandchildren rather than the other way around?

Functionally, who is honoring whom more?

Maybe this lack of notice is not even dishonor. It is, to coin a new word – unhonor. It never even crosses the child's mind to honor their grandparents.

Three Principles to Honor Grandparents
To combat this child-centeredness I offer these three suggestions. How you implement them will depend on the current age of your children, the nature of your relationship with the grandparents, and how close you live.

1. Teach your children to honor the aged. God takes one-tenth of his law to command honor of parents (Exodus 20:12). It is the only command with a promise, Paul reminds us. Even more so, by extension, we are to honor grandparents. It is good to train our children to honor us and to honor their grandparents.

When I was in school, as a sign of respect and honor, we were expected to rise when the teacher walked in. If another teacher interrupted the class, we rose when he or she came in as well. This now-quaint tradition in a secular school showed honor to those in authority over us. It was a specific application of Leviticus 19:32, "Stand in the presence of the aged, show respect for the elderly and revere the Lord your God." This verse clearly shows that honoring the aged and honoring the Lord are tied together.

All sorts of applications fall out from this principle.

- When our children are small, they should warmly greet their arriving grandparents.
- When older they should put away their electronic device and actually talk with their grandparents.
- We can give them questions to ask their grandparents. The *Donut Date Journal 2* has a number of suggestions.
- When still older they might even ask advice about issues they are facing.

There are many, many ways honor can and should flow from child to grandparent.

2. Teach your children to take the initiative in reaching out. Many grandparents will not want to impose on their grandchild's life. As a result, they are waiting for the child to invite them in. Let's encourage our children to take the initiative to ask their grandparents into their lives. This might include an invitation to sporting events or plays. It might just be texting them every now and then. Or it could involve asking them to talk with their distant grandparent on the phone.

3. Accept your role as catalyst and honor as a goal. As the parent you have a key role in encouraging this relationship. Yet, with the busyness of life and the self-centeredness of sin, this area will need constant attention. Even recently, I texted a reminder to my adult children to reach out to their grandparents. They do an excellent job in this area, but we all need reminders. Know that teaching them to appropriately honor their grandparents will give them a deeper perspective on life. It will be one more step toward thankfulness and out of self-focus.

Relationships with grandparents can be tricky. Teaching our children to honor the aged and particularly the aged closest to them pleases the Lord and is a worthwhile discipleship goal.

Understanding What God Commands

LECTURE NOTES

Parents, Know and Believe What
God Says to Your Child

God to Children: Obey and Honor Your Parents

Ephesians 6:1-3 – Children, obey your parents in the Lord, for this is right. "Honor your father and mother" (this is the first commandment with a promise) "that it may go well with you and that you may live long in the land."

Colossians 3:20 – Children, obey your parents in everything, for this pleases the Lord.

God says:

- Obedience to you is _____ .

- Honoring you is so that it may go _____ .

- Obeying you in everything _____ .

Therefore – Children _____ obey and they _____ obey.

The Parenting Paradox

" We expect them to obey because God commands it.
We expect them to disobey because they are sinful."

But that obedience is influenced by how we parent.

The Why of Teaching Our Children to Obey Us

The Two Worlds Diagram

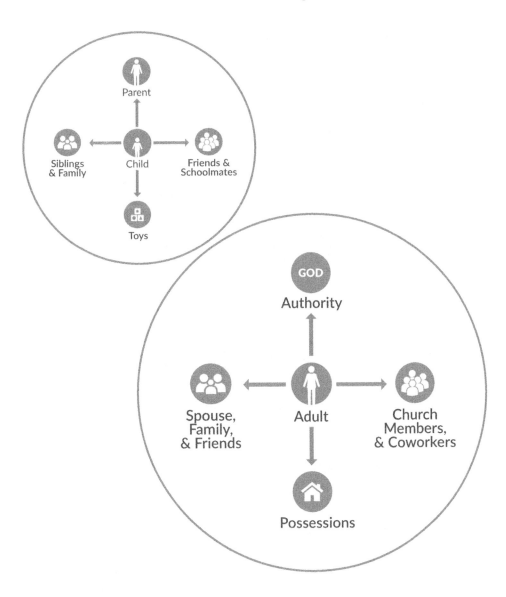

"You must not wonder that men refuse to obey their Father which is in heaven, if you allow them, when children, to disobey their father who is upon earth."

– J. C. Ryle

The How of Teaching Our Children to Obey Us

Parents, Teach and Train for First-Time Obedience

1. God's word teaches children to obey us.
- To train to not obey, is to train to disobey.

- Obedience is "all the way, right away, and in a happy way." That is a key phrase you will want to repeat over and over.

- Don't count to three. Don't tell them 10 times. You are becoming a Threatening-Repeating Parent. You are training them to ignore you.

- There are life-threatening times when our children need to obey us without question, like in a parking lot or at a street. We used the code word "Freeze." That meant just that – "Don't move." You can make a game of it to train them.

2. Speak with verbal authority using their _____.
- See the essay, *Parents, Speak with Verbal Authority.*

3. Don't end with _____
- See the essay *Parents, "OK?" is not OK.*

4. Use the appeal rule.
- This keeps the standard of obedience but keeps from exasperating them.

- They can respectfully give you some more information that you don't know about.

- This may or may not change your answer.

5. Use the five-minute warning
- Give a five-minute warning so they can power down emotionally and prepare to leave or clean up.

6. Be sure to brief and debrief for an event.
- Before you go to someone's house, talk through what to expect and how they might be tempted. Tell them what to do if there are disagreements. You are the parent, you can think ahead.

  - Afterwards, debrief on how the event went

  - See the essay *Parents, Teach Your Children to be Polite*

Parents, Know and Believe What God Says to You

Ephesians 6:4 – Fathers, do not exasperate your children, but bring them up in the training and instruction of the Lord.

Fathers

Do Not Exasperate Your Children

Ways We Can Exasperate

1. Having favorites.

2. Scolding.

3. Being inconsistent in discipline.

4. Anger out of control (See the *Parenting with Patience* study).

5. Not being willing to ask forgiveness.

6. _____ words that attack their identity.

7. Being emotionally distant.

8. Pushing for achievement beyond reason.

9. Using _____ as a tool.

Parents, Understand the Funnel Principle

But Bring Them Up...

Infant ——————————————— 12 ——————————— 21 year old
        (Childhood)   (Adult-in-training)

This!

Not this!

Of the Lord

- We need the Gospel to save.

- We need the_____ to cleanse.

- We need the Spirit to empower.

See the short essays on the following pages:

- *Parents, Speak with Verbal Authority*

- *Parents, "OK?" Is Not OK*

- *Parents, Train Your Children to Be Polite*

NOTES

NOTES

REFLECTION QUESTIONS

Use the following questions to guide your discussion.

1. Do you have difficulty expecting obedience from your children? Why or why not? What difference does it make that God commands your children to obey and honor you?

2. Do you tend to excuse disobedience? What do you usually say?

3. Do you struggle with anger because you are surprised at your children's disobedience? How does the parenting paradox help?

4. Do your children come when called? Do they look at you and pay attention when you speak to them? Is your child saying "No" to you? What have you done about it?

5. Are there any areas of disobedience or dishonor that are not pleasing to the Lord? List all of them you can think of. This list will guide our application. We will not tackle them all at once. But put them all down on paper.

ESSAYS

Parents, Speak with Verbal Authority

Verbal authority. Some people have it. Some people need to develop it.

My mother, at 5'7" and slight of build, taught high school English. She was a tough and effective teacher. Over the years she has had many students tell her she was their favorite high school teacher.

But don't doubt that she was in control of her classroom. She had football players weighing twice as much as her completely under her control. Her greatest challenge? One year she had an afternoon class of thirty hormonal football players and flirty cheerleaders.

She exerted her authority ... and they learned English.

Her example inspired me when I taught high school for a few years. And it should inspire you. A teacher, a pastor, and yes, a parent, needs to understand and be comfortable exercising authority for the good of his/her sheep.

How do you speak to young children with authority? Though I cannot point to a chapter and verse, these suggestions come from some years of experience. Child training is parent training. Here are some ways to train ourselves.

Five Suggestions

1. Use your child's name to get his attention. Children are often busy and deeply engrossed in their play. Their name should and will cut through the clutter. Make sure you have your child's attention before giving a command.

> For example –
> *"Anthony?"*
> *"Yes, Mom?"*
> *"Would you go outside and get your sister?"*
> *"Yes, Mom."*

2. Make sure they can hear you. It should go without saying that we speak in a way that they can hear us. If they are upstairs, don't yell from the kitchen. Walk to the bottom of the stairs.

3. If they are where they can see you, in most cases they should also look at you. This is just polite. But our attention also goes where we look. So if we give commands without them looking at us, it probably has not cut through the clutter of the day.

4. Train them to give you verbal positive response. I cover this extensively in the next essay, *Parents, "OK?" is not OK.* But there will probably be many conversations like this.

> *"Anthony?"*
> *"Yes, Mom."*
> *"We are going to leave in five minutes. It's time to get ready. (Understand?)"*
> *"Yes, Mom."*

5. Don't use "OK?". Use "Understand?"

Don't use, "Clean up your room, OK?"
Instead say, "Jason, I want you to put your toys away. Do you understand me?"
"Yes, Mom."

6. Watch for obedience and notice disobedience. As parents we give many instructions throughout the day. It can be tiring. But we need to carefully observe what we are saying and what the response is. God is not a Threatening-Repeating Parent and neither should we be. He says what he means and means what he says. And so should we. Authority is enforced by consequences.

How Do I Train this Verbal Response Habit?
But how do I train my children to give me eye-attention and verbal-attention? Simply refuse to go to the next step until they give you their attention. Repeat if necessary.

> *"Anthony and Lisa, let me have your attention."*
> Pause.
> *"Look at me please and say 'Yes, Mom.'"*
> *"Yes, Mom."*
> *"That's better. Would you please..... Do you understand me?"*

As parents, we are constantly, constantly training. At some point we may decide that this has become an issue of disrespect and disobedience and start to have consequences for it. But at the beginning, it is train, train, and retrain.

For further reading on the why of discipline, read Chapter 7 of *The Disciple-Making Parent – Preparing Your Children for the Gospel.*

Parents, "OK?" Is Not OK

The heart of *The Disciple-Making Parent* is helping parents pass the gospel to and disciple their children. Inevitably that spills over into what we might call Parenting 101.

Early in this video series, I made the Study Bible analogy. In a Study Bible, there are inspired words from God that you may not argue with, only seek to understand and obey. There are also words that are commentary from fallible men and women. These ideas are not inspired but come from wisdom.

I offer the following suggestion knowing that it fits squarely in the "Study Bible Notes" part of parenting. I cannot point to a chapter and verse to back it up but I think it represents wisdom.

"OK?" is Not OK

As I observe parents giving commands to their small children, I often hear them ending with the question, "OK?"

For example, "Alex, give that toy back to Sarah. OK?" or "Jonathan, it's time to go. I want you to start cleaning up your toys. OK?"

I don't like this word pattern because of what it implies. It takes a command that should be obeyed and then softens it. In essence, we are asking our child, "Is that OK with you?" It carries the tone of, "I am giving you a command. But it has to be OK with you. You have to want to do it. If it is not OK, then don't do it."

I believe that our young children internalize that message. They become the arbitrator of whether they will obey the command or not.

Positively, underneath this question is a desire not to be a military parent who goes around barking orders. We want to have an openness to more information. Those are good impulses. But I don't think they outweigh the possible negative message our children might hear.

"Understand?"

Let me suggest an alternative that both engages a young child after a command and yet does not seem to offer him a choice. It rightly places him or her under our authority.

It is the question – "Understand?"

Thus, a script might go like this:

> "Alex?"
> "Yes Mom."
> Give that toy back to Sarah. Understand?"
> "Yes, Mom."

Or

> "Jonathan?"
> "Yes Dad."
> "It's time to go. Start cleaning up your toys. Do you understand me?"
> "Yes Dad."

This type of script should be going on tens or even hundreds of times a day. There is:

    1. A call for their attention with a response.
    2. A reasonable command.
    3. A question asking for their response and obtaining it.

The Appeal Rule

This also works well when combined with the appeal rule. The appeal rule allows a child to say something like, "Please may I appeal?" or "Please may I ask why?" It allows the child to offer more information that the parent might not know about and prevents frustration.

For example, in our scenarios above, Alex might say,

> "Please may I appeal Mom?"
> "What is it, Alex?"
> "Sarah told me she was through playing with the toy."

Or Jonathan might say,

> "Please may I appeal Dad?"
> "What is it Jonathan?"
> "I am almost done building my tower. Can I just have some more time?"

Thus, there is an outlet for an appeal.

Conclusion

Loving parents try to combine asking for a response and an openness to more information by packing too much into the word, "OK?" Instead of giving the child the authority to choose, retain that authority by asking "Understand?" and having the appeal rule as an option.

I do not believe our child's eternal destiny lies on whether we do this as a family. And we don't want to judge others. But it does line up with the understanding of training our children to live under our authority.

This pattern was a blessing to our family. Try it! I think you will be blessed.

Parents, Train Your Children to Be Polite

Has basic politeness fallen on hard times? Some would say that these issues are not important. After all, what do greeting and thanking have to do with the gospel?

But Scripture tells us **Love is not rude** (1 Corinthians 13:4). Stated positively, love expresses itself in consideration of others. Godliness and manners are close friends. Manners are a cultural way of showing consideration to others.

While certainly not the most foundational way we train our children, teaching them to consider others is not unimportant.

Seven Practical Suggestions for Teaching Your Children to Be Polite

1. Teach your children to greet adults. Did you know that Christians are commanded to greet one another? It is one of the simplest forms of love. Teach your children to greet adults especially when they are spoken to. Do not excuse them by saying they are shy. It is a joy to watch children and adults interact in this simple way.

2. Teach your children to thank adults for hosting them. Thankfulness is also a training issue. When visiting at a friend's house, let's make sure we encourage them to interact with the host of the event. Again, even small children can be expected to say a simple, "Thank you," to adults.

3. Teach your children to use words like "Please" and "Thank you." Do we really need to say this? Children should be trained to use these words in the home and with us. Then they will much more naturally use them outside the home.

4. Teach your children to speak respectfully to you and other adults. The Bible is clear that we are to show respect for age. I grew up in the South, where there is the cultural habit of saying, "Yes, Sir" and "Yes, Ma'am." Although we did not feel like we could expect this for our children growing up in the Northeast, they were required to say, "Yes, Dad" or "Yes, Mom." "Yep" and "Nope" were not allowed.

In addition, though some may disagree, I think another way to communicate that respectful honor is by using last names. It communicates a proper distance and respect in the relationship.

5. Practice appropriate table manners. I am not arguing for some dainty, Victorian, milquetoast manners. But basic table manners are a way to be considerate for everyone around.

6. Teach your children how to politely interrupt you. At some point, all children will need to get their parent's attention while they are talking with another adult. Will they rudely tug on your arm or march right up and start the conversation? One suggestion that we and our friends implemented was to train our children to put their hand on our shoulder (if sitting) or on our hip (if standing). This let us know they wanted to talk with us. And it allowed us to wait until a break in the conversation to address them.

7. Practice these yourself. Children will imitate what they see modeled. We cannot expect our children to speak kindly if we are not doing the same. Is there some basic habit of politeness that I need to grow in as I speak to my spouse and children?

Politeness is simply a matter of thinking highly of others. Your children can be taught these things.

LESSON
4

Understanding Training and Instruction

LECTURE NOTES

Parents, Know Your Tools, How to Use Them, and How They Change Over Time

...bring them up in the training and instruction of the Lord. (Eph 6:4)

	Instruction (Depth of Words)	Training (Action)
Positive	Teaching, Encouragement, A_____	Positive Rehearsal, R_____
Negative	Rebuke, Correction, Admonition, Warning	Natural consequences Artificial consequences

How Training and Instruction Change Over Time

Parents, Use Action More Than Words for Young Children

- Action is not words.
- Action is action.
- See the essay, *Parents, Think about How Parenting Changes Over the Years*

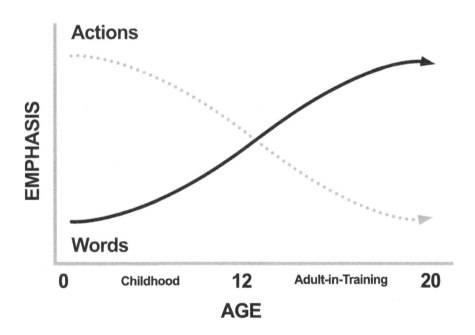

Parents, Understand the Biblical Pattern of Change: Putting Off and Putting On

The Biblical Pattern of Change is...

Ephesians 4:22-24
> *to put off your old self, which belongs to your former manner of life and is corrupt through deceitful desires, **and to be renewed** in the spirit of your minds, **and to put on** the new self, created after the likeness of God in true righteousness and holiness.*

- **Put off** the negative.
- **Renew** the mind.
- **Put on** the positive.

Parents, Train, Train, and Retrain

Example of training to come when called.
- Don't - instruct, expect obedience, and then discipline for disobedience.
- Do - instruct, make a game of coming when called, continue positive training, and then later work on disobedience.

Example of dealing with complaining or tattle telling.
- Don't – get angry or ignore.
- Do – give out consequences and require the positive. "Go on the blue chair and come back with four things you are thankful for your brother."
- Build "Muscle-memory" through positive rehearsal.

Parents, Train in Private for Peace in Public
- Home is the training ground.
- Public (another home, restaurant, church) is the testing ground.
- Ask, "When we are in public, do others enjoy my children?" or are they annoying others? Though children can be immature, we need to be considerate of others.

Parents, Be Comfortable Shaping the Will Through Joyful Conflict

- All this presupposes we are comfortable and know we are called to shape the will through joyful conflict.
- God shapes our will through hard times. God says "No" plenty. God disciplines us. God corrects us.
- See the essay, *Parents, Give Them Grace By Giving Them the Law.*

Case Study: The Interrupting Child

Parents, Rest on The Three-Legged Stool

The Family Principles Poster

- Write out positive qualities we are aiming for. (More information in the next pages.)

The Character Chart

- Write out actions and attitudes we are working on. (More information in the next pages.)

The Shepherds' Meeting

- Create a habit that keeps Dad and Mom calmly communicating and on the same page. (More information in the next pages.)

The Family Principles Poster

We love, honor and obey Jesus Christ in all that we do:
- By growing in His Word
- By worshipping Him with our whole heart
- By inviting Him to be on the throne of our heart during the day
- By growing in our character

We love, honor and obey Dad and Mom in all that we do:
- By obeying right away, all the way and in a happy way.
- By not rebelling against their authority but appealing to them
- By not grumbling or complaining but being joyful
- By listening to Dad and Mom's wisdom

We love and honor each other:
- By not getting angry but being patient
- By not stealing but asking kindly
- By not arguing with each other but appealing to Dad and Mom
- By not being selfish but including others
- By not interrupting but listening

We do all the work that God has assigned to us:
- By doing all the schoolwork for the day
- By doing all the chores for the day
- By keeping our bodies, our house and our room orderly

We keep ourselves pure:
- By not letting others entice us into sin
- By reading and watching only what Dad and Mom would approve
- By confessing our sins to God
- By representing Jesus when we go out to public places

We accept the consequences when we fail in any of these areas:
- By learning from the discipline
- By asking for God's grace in changing
- By listening to Dad and Mom's correction

Download poster at **ParentingwithConfidenceStudy.com/bonuses**

Parents, Have a Plan and Keep Track of Correction Using a Character Chart

Who	What to Put Off	Consequence	What to Put On	Scripture
N	Not Obeying	Chastisement	Obeying all the way, right away, and with a happy spirit	Ephesians 6:1, Colossians 3:20
R, C	Tattletaling	Chair for 3 minutes	Mom, I think you ought to know about....	Proverbs 26:22, 20
K	Telling a Lie	Chastisement	Truthfulness	
K, C, R, N	Interrupting	Chair for 3 minutes. Then retry.	Listening, Self-Control	Proverbs 18: 13
C	Disrespect	Chastisement	Respectful appeal	Exodus 20:12
K, C, R, N	Delayed Chore Obedience	Extra chore	Immediate obedience or	Colossians 3:20
K, C	Complaining about the others	4 Thankful things	Thankfulness for your brother	

Who	What to Put Off	Consequence	What to Put On	Scripture

Download chart at **ParentingwithConfidenceStudy.com/bonuses**

Parents, For Older Children, Include the Heart on the Character Chart

Biblically, the heart is the target.

The heart can...
- Love God or hate God.
- Believe or disbelieve.
- Grow hard.
- Be deceived.
- Turn away or open wide.
- Set up idols to serve.

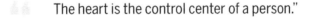 The heart is the control center of a person."

Heart Attitudes

- Generosity vs Coveting
- Loving Others vs Loving Ourselves
- Humility vs Pride
- Fearing God vs Fearing Man
- Seeking God's Approval vs Seeking Man's
- Submitting vs Rebelling
- Honoring vs Dishonoring
- Peacemaking vs Ungodly Anger

 Sinful behavior reveals heart attitudes."

The character chart grows deeper as the heart of our child grows deeper.

Parents, Make Sure the Shepherds are Meeting on a "Coffee Date"

The Notebook

The "Coffee Date"

How did we do this?

1. We had a small notebook in the kitchen to write down the things we wanted to talk about on this date. There were several benefits to this. It allowed both of us to write down decisions we needed to make or problems we needed to talk about. For example, if we saw a new behavior pattern in one child, we didn't have to bring it up in the moment. We could just write it down to be talked about.

A second benefit was it allowed both of us to preview the list before we went out. This meant that if we were going to talk about a touchy subject at least we had a chance to brace ourselves so we would react in a godly way.

2. We had the day marked regularly in our calendar. At times it was weekly, and at other times it was every two weeks. This meant that it did not get squeezed out by other activities. Or if it did get replaced, at least we realized it.

3. We went out for coffee. For a babysitter, we had a family who lived next door who could walk to us. If the babysitter is a logistical or financial challenge, consider trading off babysitting with another couple. It was important for us to get out of the house.

We deliberately just went out for coffee instead of a full meal. Why? We wanted to create a sustainable, regular habit on our tight budget. In addition, we separated this time from our other "dates." A full meal or an event is a time for us to reconnect as a couple. The coffee date is like a family shepherd business meeting. Its goal is to make decisions, not necessarily reconnect.

4. We started with prayer. When we went out, we prayed together in the car to start our evening. With young children, there were times we were falling asleep in the car!

5. We talked through the notebook. In the coffee shop, I took the lead to go over the things on our list to talk about. We tried to leave with decisions made or plans made on all the things on our list.

The Benefits
This regular coffee date had numerous benefits. It pulled my focus back into the family. It reminded me that I was a dad leading a family not just a pastor. It pulled

Sharon's focus off of the children and back on me. It reminded her she was a wife not just a mom. And it sent a message to the children that Mom and Dad care for each other and are taking time for their relationship.

Over time the frequency changed as the schedules changed, but the essence was there.

Does every couple need to follow this pattern? Obviously not. But many family shepherds would benefit from this routine. Just as church shepherds benefit from regular meetings, so family shepherds need to sit down and discuss how their sheep are doing.

See the short essays on the following pages:

- *Parents, Think about How Parenting Changes Over the Years*

- *Parents, Give Them Grace By Giving Them the Law*

NOTES

PARENTING WITH CONFIDENCE

REFLECTION QUESTIONS

Use the following questions to guide your discussion.

1. How is the marriage partnership on this issue of training? Wives are you bypassing your husbands? Husbands are you being passive and just wanting to play with the kids?

2. How old are your children? Have you given too many freedoms? Is the funnel too wide? Or have you been overly strict with the funnel too narrow?

3. Do you tend to overuse action or words in your house or jump back and forth?

4. Regarding words, are your children more aware of your correction or your affections?

5. Do your children know the positive that is expected of them? Might the Family Principles Poster help in your house?

6. Can you see how the Character Chart might work in your family situation? What are some problems that you are facing that you could put on the list?

7. Read the essay *Parents, Give Them Grace by Giving Them the Law.* Have you felt uncomfortable shaping the will through conflict because you are afraid of messing them up? What does this essay make clear?

ESSAYS

Parents, Think about How Parenting Changes Over the Years

Thoughts for Parents

1. God is in your parenting.
2. Are you praying together for wisdom?
3. Do you have a regular coffee date?
4. Are you a dictator? Or do you operate like a balanced government - Legislative, Executive, Judicial?
5. Dad, are you listening to Mom? Mom, are you communicating with Dad?
6. Are you talking to others (grandparents, older church members, pastors)?
7. Are you repenting yourself? Parenting is to make you more holy.

Thoughts for Younger Children (0-6)

1. Order, routine, control is good; Small funnel is good.
2. Disobedience is to be expected and serious.
3. "No" from them is treason, to be expected and serious.
4. Discipline should sting.
5. Build margin to discipline into your schedule.
6. Crying is OK.
7. "No" from you is fine.
8. Limit media use.
9. God gave you LITTLE children for a reason. Gain their heart and obedience while they are small.
10. Amount of Action > Amount of Explanation

Thoughts for Older Children (7-12)

1. Enjoy! If you have done hard work in the early years, these are great years. If not, it's not too late.
2. Connect to the heart. Check out *The Donut Date Journal.*
3. Keep going with the consequences.
4. Place a high value on family unity – meanness not allowed, chores for meanness to the other, etc.
5. Make sure to use the put off/made new/put on pattern.
6. Amount of Action = Amount of Explanation.

Thoughts for Teens (12/13-18)

1. Are you making time to listen?
2. Are you asking questions to understand your young adult?

3. Are you picking your battles?

4. Are you bringing grace and the Word of God to bear?

5. Do they know you love them no matter what?

6. Do they know that working leads to eating, "You don't work, you don't eat," (2 Thess 3:10). This means, "I am providing you with benefits of living under my roof. Are you taking care of your responsibilities?"

7. Amount of Action < Amount of Explanation.

Parents, Give Them Grace By Giving Them the Law

I have noticed a good but misguided desire among many young Christian parents. They seek to be intentional in the way they raise their children. Many have an excellent desire to be more gospel-focused. They want to treat their children the way that God is treating them – with grace. So they draw a direct line from this grace and want to parent with grace.

Unfortunately, using just this paradigm for parenting flattens the gospel. When we look at the whole of Scripture we see that God adopted Israel as his son and called him out of Egypt. The Scripture tells us that God then placed Israel, his son, under the law for a time. When the proper time came, Israel would be released from the law. Galatians tells us that the law was like a tutor of a young child. It was a guardian put there until the child had grown up (Gal 3:24).

Theologians historically have seen three good purposes of the law:

First, the law shows us our need of a Savior. God tells us that the greatest commandments are to love him and to love our neighbor. But how do we do that? The law spells out the *how* of loving God and neighbor. And when we don't fulfill it, we realize that we are sinful and need a Savior.

Second, the law restrains sin. It is a fence or rope that holds back sinful behavior. The law cannot change the heart. But the threat of punishment does create civil order.

Third, the law shows those who have a changed heart how to please Christ. It is the railroad tracks that tell us how to run. When God changes a heart so that it is born again, new desires to please God are given to it.

The law, for all its inadequacies, was still a good thing. It was the tutor that prepared the nation for the grace of Christ. It taught them basic lessons about God's holiness, atonement, and love for others. If God had revealed Jesus to the nation at Mount Sinai, it would have made no sense. The young nation needed the grace of the law before they needed the grace of freedom.

Law and Order in the Home
The purposes of the law are similar in our homes.

First, our law will also show our children their need for a Savior. Our young children need to learn to live under our law. There need to be rules which they are expected to obey and where there are consequences when they disobey. This dynamic of commands, obedience, and disobedience inculcates a sense of their need for a Savior.

Second, living under our law also restrains natural childlike disobedience. It creates a civil society in the home where there is order. The law cannot change the heart. But it can create a peaceful home without lawlessness. Having wild children is not a sign of grace and godliness. Wild and disobedient children are a black mark for a man and his leadership (Titus 1:6).

Third, living under our law also trains our children to please Christ. Paul explicitly commands children to obey their parents, for this is pleasing to the Lord (Eph 6:4). Obedience that is pleasing requires rules and commands from parents. Our children are trained in habits that a regenerate heart will delight to follow.

Some may object, "But shouldn't I show my children grace?" Absolutely! Show them the grace of love. The grace of affection. The grace of calmness. The grace of order. And the grace of consequences.

Letting our children disobey us without consequences is not a sign of grace but a sign of hate (Rev 3:19). Living under the law prepared a people for the grace of Jesus Christ. In a similar way, bringing our young children under submission to our rules prepares them to know the grace of the Lord Jesus.

And just as the time came for the law to be replaced because its purpose was fulfilled, so a time will come for our family laws to fall away.

Gospel-parenting does not negate the law. It includes it.

Understanding The Need for Habits, Routine, Rules, and Self-Discipline

LECTURE NOTES

Parents, Structure the Environment

Children Need Love and Affection

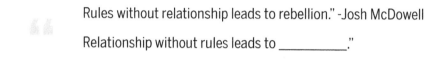

Rules without relationship leads to rebellion." -Josh McDowell

Relationship without rules leads to _____."

Children Need Formative Discipline

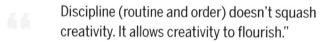

Discipline (routine and order) doesn't squash creativity. It allows creativity to flourish."

Check out the essay, *Parents, Know How Routines Will Help You Thrive* for more suggestions on routines.

A Few Examples of Our Family Rules

See these essays on the following pages:
- *Parents, Ask Question to Remind Your Children about Family Rules.*
- *Parents, Have a Media Plan and Monitor Their Media.*

Parents, Calm the Chaos and Don't Be a Bedraggled Parent

Keep Your Marriage _____
- Your marriage is the primary relationship.
- You and your marriage, not the children, are the center of your family.
- You were a wife long before you were a mother. You will be afterwards. Nurture it through date nights, weekends away, etc.
- Don't forget to care for your physical relationship with your spouse.

Don't Be a Bedraggled Mother
- *You are not a more loving mother by constantly following your child around!*
- Routine, boundaries (pack-n-play), and timers can be your best friends.
- Take care of yourself. Make sure you have social contact with other adults and keep ministering in church.
- Don't forget to care for your physical body.

Other Ways to Help
Pack-n-Plays are a Mom's and child's best friend
- Pack-n-plays are an essential tool for a mom's sanity.
- They provide order to a small child's world.
- They provide safety for the child. They also allow you to do other things for yourself, confident your child is ok.
- Start very early – 6 months.
- Put two or three toys in and it becomes their safe place.

Timers are Your Friends
- They are an outside authority.
- They also provide structure to your day.
- We would say, "Go outside for 30 minutes." "Sit on the chair for 3 minutes." "Practice piano for 30 minutes." Then we would set a timer.

Get Your Infant on a Sleeping Routine
- You *can* train your children to sleep through the night.
- *All four of our children slept through the night by 8 weeks – even one with a bad case of colic!*

For Help with Sleep Training

 The Disciple-Making Parent Podcast Episode #20 - A Baby's First Year.

NOTES

REFLECTION QUESTIONS

Use the following questions to guide your discussion.

1. Does the idea of routine and structure sound attractive or do you resist it? Why? What would be some good outcomes for having routine in your life?

2. How can routines and clear rules cut down on the number of conflicts in the family?

3. What are some clear rules you have already? Where do you need to add some?

4. What current conflicts in your family do you have that could be solved by a new family policy? For example, "Mom and Dad have decided that we are not going to _____ anymore." How will you communicate and enforce that new policy?

5. If your children are younger, are you using structure in the environment like a pack-n-play, a gate, or other structures? Why or why not?

ESSAYS

Parents, Ask Questions to Remind Your Children About Family Rules

I came across a cartoon recently that was a reminder of a helpful parenting strategy that I think reinforces biblical values. In it, a child comes to his grandfather asking for candy. His grandfather asks the boy, "What is our rule?" The boy dejectedly responds, "No candy before dinner." Grandpa corrects him. "That is Grandma's rule. Grandpa's rule is to bring me a piece too!" I hope to make that my rule someday!

This illustrates a simple strategy:

- **Respond to a request by asking the child to remember a family rule or principle.**
- **Or ask a question to remind them about what they should be doing.**

For example:
> *"Mom. I'm hungry. Can I get some chips?"*
> *"What is our rule about snacks between meals?"*
> *"We only have fruit or carrots between meals."*
> *"OK, well there's your answer. Would you like some slices of apple?"*

Or

> *"Dad, do I have to go to bed now?"*
> *"What's your bedtime?"*
> *"8pm."*
> *"Well, it's 8pm so you know the answer to that question."*

Reminding
This technique can be used to encourage our children to be responsible without a direct command. It is an easy way to provide a reminder.

> *"Hon, I noticed you left your toys in the yard after you played outside. What are you supposed to do when you are done playing?"*
> *"Put them away."*
> *"That's right. Go do that right now."*

Benefits
There are multiple benefits to asking questions like these.
1. Jesus often used questions to teach and remind. Questions can sneak past our natural defenses and cause us to think more deeply.

2. Questions appeal to a higher authority. Mom and Dad, in their calmer moments, have established rules that are there to bless the family and to give it order. Everything in the family is not up for grabs. In the moment, we are simply reminding our children. Mom and Dad are not being capricious.

3. This appeal to outside authority also inculcates more self-control in our children. It trains their conscience. They know what they are supposed to do in a certain situation. They may not do it. But they know what they are expected to do.

4. It also forces Mom and Dad to come up with principles. Often anger in a family is the result of not establishing enough outside family principles. When a question comes up, rather than acting randomly, Mom or Dad ought to think, "What is the principle here?"

Conclusion

Don't feel the need to ask questions all the time. There are certainly occasions for direct commands and correction. And there are times for direct answers of *yes*, *no*, or more information.

But establishing family routines and rules and then reminding our children when they forget should be a frequent tool of every wise parent.

Parents, Think About Your Baby's First Year and Beyond

Dr. Tom Hines has been a pediatrician in Lincoln RI for the past 30 years. He and his wife have four adult children. I asked him to comment on some of the issues we have been talking about. The following is taken from some comments he made to me in several interviews.

What's the biggest change you have seen in parenting over the years?

Parents are parenting out of fear. Fear of not doing things right. Fear of messing up their children. Fear of not giving them every advantage. A lot of that fear comes from listening to many voices, not the voice of the Shepherd.

Parents often say, "I don't want to squash their creativity" or "If I don't let them wander everywhere it will squash them." What is your perspective?

Children need structure and limitation. They need to work and play with limitations. They expect it. They want it. They are more secure when they have it. Because in that structured, secure environment they have the freedom to become creative.

A huge problem of older children is that they will never sit still. Parents are forever chasing their children. But they have never been trained to sit still and play quietly.

I'm a huge fan of pack-n-plays. From the time a child is 4 to 6 months start putting them in there. Let them explore the confines of their environment. The child doesn't care. They think of it as their old friend, their place of security. Once a child is already crawling there is going to be a more difficulty. When our children were very young they would play for up to an hour in the pack-n-play!

Parents often don't want their children to cry or fuss.

When I deal with sleep issues, I will often ask, "What is the longest you have let your children cry?" They usually reply, "Well, we don't let them cry." It's because they have read too much. They think they are causing them psychological damage.

Parents think to ignore a child's wishes is causing harm to their child. I am not talking about true neglect. But parents are afraid they are causing harm. For example, if you have a 9-month-old that's been in the pack-n-play for 20 minutes and he starts to fuss a little bit, just wait a minute. If you immediately jump to rescue him and pull him out, you are teaching him that if he fusses, it will deliver him.

Whiny children are whiny for a reason. It works. But if you ignore it from day one, he will learn that it doesn't work. He will go back to playing. Then pick them up. Appropriately ignore your child when you should. Parents respond because they are embarrassed or fearful. It's OK to make them wait. It's OK to let them cry a little. It's OK to let them be a little bored.

The things we think are a big deal aren't. It is harder for us than them. They don't remember it!

What do you think about sleep training? I feel so burdened about this because families are still not getting sleep months after they have had the baby. We had some good teaching and all our babies slept through the night by eight weeks.

One of the things I like to help parents with is that once weight gain is established, feeding is established, and they are through that crazy first one to two weeks, is to really get them to start thinking about putting that baby on a routine or a schedule of some sort, both for their good and also for the good of the baby. There's been a lot of controversy through the years about how you can't spoil a baby or you can't get a baby on a routine. You're going to hear a lot of things, really do a lot of different things, but by the end of the first month, you can definitely have a baby on some semblance of a routine or schedule. It may not be perfect, but what I try to help parents do in that first month is to know what to aim for and how to get there.

So what kinds of things do I tell a parent? Well, it's not rocket science, but if you want the baby to be in bed by eight or nine o'clock, you need to start their day by eight or nine o'clock this morning. It's not rocket science. So you pick a time and you say, "Gee, I would like this to be the start of the day for this baby." And then going forward, there's things that I share with them in terms of a schedule. But I would just say it's understanding that babies can be put on a schedule and just letting that sink into a parent. But, you start the day the same. It's what you do between those two points in time- from the time they get up to the time they go to bed- that's key. But the importance of a schedule just brings the home back to some sense of normalcy by the first couple of months. Because again, having a baby disrupts everything, disrupt schedule, sleep for both the parents and everybody else involved.

What do you think about creativity and boredom?

I worry about parents using electronics as the instant pacifier or sedative. The children are running around like crazy and then boom, the electronics calm them down. Cell phones are becoming this also.

We believe that boredom is bad and our children have to be entertained all the time. Instead of the child learning to entertain themselves, that creativity is zapped. The parents are in a trap. When they try to turn the TV or electronic off, the child fusses again.

Boredom is the wellspring of creativity. The more we distract them, the more they don't know what to do when they are bored. Buy toys of substance.

For Help with Sleep Training and to Hear More from Dr. Hines

 Check out The Disciple-Making Parent Podcast **Episode #20** – A Baby's First Year. **Episode #1 and 2** – Advice from a Seasoned Christian Pediatrician

What's the biggest change you have seen in parenting over the years?

Parents are parenting out of fear. Fear of not doing things right. Fear of messing up their children. Fear of not giving them every advantage. A lot of that fear comes from listening to many voices, not the voice of the Shepherd.

Parents often say, "I don't want to squash their creativity" or "If I don't let them wander everywhere it will squash them." What is your perspective?

Children need structure and limitation. They need to work and play with limitations. They expect it. They want it. They are more secure when they have it. Because in that structured, secure environment they have the freedom to become creative.

A huge problem of older children is that they will never sit still. Parents are forever chasing their children. But they have never been trained to sit still and play quietly.

I'm a huge fan of pack-n-plays. From the time a child is 4 to 6 months start putting them in there. Let them explore the confines of their environment. The child doesn't care. They think of it as their old friend, their place of security. Once a child is already crawling there is going to be a more difficulty. When our children were very young they would play for up to an hour in the pack-n-play!

Parents often don't want their children to cry or fuss.

When I deal with sleep issues, I will often ask, "What is the longest you have let your children cry?" They usually reply, "Well, we don't let them cry." It's because they have read too much. They think they are causing them psychological damage.

Parents think to ignore a child's wishes is causing harm to their child. I am not talking about true neglect. But parents are afraid they are causing harm. For example, if you have a 9-month-old that's been in the pack-n-play for 20 minutes and he starts to fuss a little bit, just wait a minute. If you immediately jump to rescue him and pull him out, you are teaching him that if he fusses, it will deliver him.

Whiny children are whiny for a reason. It works. But if you ignore it from day one, he will learn that it doesn't work. He will go back to playing. Then pick them up. Appropriately ignore your child when you should. Parents respond because they are embarrassed or fearful. It's OK to make them wait. It's OK to let them cry a little. It's OK to let them be a little bored.

The things we think are a big deal aren't. It is harder for us than them. They don't remember it!

Parents, Have a Media Plan and Monitor Their Media

Any study on the media is going to be outdated as soon as it is released. But one study found teens were using NINE hours of media use a day not including texting, school and homework. Another study put it at 11 because teens were multitasking. More than 70% said they had TVs in the bedrooms and 66% reported a TV on during the meals. Not surprisingly only about one-half of parents had rules for media use.

As anyone who knows a teen or tween can attest, media is among the most powerful forces in young people's lives today. The TV shows they watch, video games they play, songs they listen to, books they read and websites they visit are an enormous part of their lives, offering a constant stream of messages about families, peers, relationships, gender roles, sex, violence, food, and values. Neil Postman said that the TV curriculum competes with the school curriculum and nearly obliterates it.

Media can be a very powerful tool for good or evil.

The Teaching of Jesus

Jesus said,

> [6] *"If anyone causes one of these little ones—those who believe in me—to stumble, it would be better for them to have a large millstone hung around their neck and to be drowned in the depths of the sea.* [7] *Woe to the world because of the things that cause people to stumble! Such things must come, but woe to the person through whom they come!"*
>
> [8] *"If your hand or your foot causes you to stumble, cut it off and throw it away. It is better for you to enter life maimed or crippled than to have two hands or two feet and be thrown into eternal fire.* [9] *And if your eye causes you to stumble, gouge it out and throw it away. It is better for you to enter life with one eye than to have two eyes and be thrown into the fire of hell." (Matthew 18:6-9)*

Disciple-making parents will equip their children to rule over this temptation.

Here are twelve suggestions to consider.

1. Be intentional in your own media use. Are you always watching TV? Are you always checking your phone? What are your kids learning by watching you?

2. Be intentional about any media you allow in your home. Don't put TVs in the bedroom. Don't put screens in the bedroom.

3. Don't give them more responsibility than they can handle. Don't worry about being counter-cultural. Start them out on a "dumb" phone. There is nothing wrong with that. A smart phone is very powerful and very addictive. If they are laughed at, tell them it's good for them. Are they going to be a leader or a lemming? You are training them to be a leader.

4. When you take the next step to more freedom, make sure they understand the responsibility that goes with it. I would suggest having some sort of written contract. Kids forget that all the benefits you give them are just that – benefits.

5. Make sure they know that it is your phone. My children didn't own a cell phone until they were 18. I, however, owned six cell phones that I lent them to use. See the difference? We need to remind our kids of this.

A well-known comedian tells a story about his kids coming home from school and being teased about how rich they were. He responded, "Your mother and I are rich. You are very, very poor." He was making the point that the children lived off the generosity of the parents. We should have this attitude too! You are the parent, aren't you? This should go for grandparents too. I would suggest that it is wise for extended family NOT to give your children electronics. Otherwise, your children will think these devices are theirs.

6. Make sure you have filters and controls in your house. We should have controls in our house like Covenant Eyes or Disney Circle. The Internet is a sewer line plugged into your home and device. Are you going to filter it or let it pour into the heart of your child?

7. Have family rules. Besides an individual agreement (see #4), what are your family rules? It is your house. You might set up rules of time like 30 minutes a day for a certain electronic device. You might set up rules of place. One family I know has a basket and when kids come over with phones, they all go in the basket. With changing technology, our family rules are out of date now. But you need to control technology or it will control you and your family.

8. Be in a community that will work with you. When your kids think you are strange because you aren't doing what everyone else is doing, you want to be able to point to other families and say, "Well, we are strange but so are the Smiths and the Joneses and the Johnsons." Talk with the youth leaders and the teachers of your kids who are keeping up with the latest problems.

9. Make sure you are talking to them on your dates, listening to them, and asking hard questions. Ask them about what they have seen. Ask them to tell you about any cyberbullying they know about.

10. Have family fasts. In *The Tech-Wise Family*, Andy Crouch argues for fasting, "One hour a day, one day a week, and one week a year." Another wise father of three children has a media free week once a month. Our kids want this structure and freedom.

11. Go after the heart. Media magnifies our idols. Is our temptation lust, money, gossip, fear of man, loving approval, coveting a lifestyle? The media we chose amplifies and feeds our idols.

12. Assume they have seen explicit content. That is beyond the scope of this essay. We don't want to be naïve but move toward this awkward conversation.

We need to take Jesus' warning seriously.

> [7] "Woe to the world because of the things that cause people to stumble! Such things must come, but woe to the person through whom they come! [8] If your hand or your foot causes you to stumble, cut it off and throw it away" (Matt 18:7-8).

Parents, Know How Routines Will Help You Thrive

The following short essay can help you thrive. You may not do everything in it but many of the principles will help. You don't have to be an exhausted mom or dad!

I had just finished a conversation with a young mom in our church. And I was discouraged. She's a great mom and had just recently given birth to her third child. We were at a summer church outreach with a little time to talk while the outreach was going on.

When I asked her how it was going, she was brutally honest. "It's hard." "The six-year-old and the three-year-old want my attention. And, of course, I have to give my ten-week-old attention."

I thanked her from her honesty and thought back to the days when our four children were young. When Nate was born, Rebekah was two, Chapman was four, and Kara was six. You can do the math. The next year: 7, 5, 3, 1. The next year: 8, 6, 4, 2. And so on.

Our household was busy, crazy, loud, messy, and fun. And yes, for the first year of Nate's life, my favorite verse was Hebrews 4:16 *Let us approach the throne of grace that we may find help in our time of need*. But based on Sharon's years as an elementary teacher and out of self-defense, our family developed routines and systems that cut down on the chaos.

No, I didn't say eliminate the chaos. We still had some crazy times. But they were less than you may think. And they were less than this mom was experiencing.

What was the solution? Routine!

The Blessing of Routines

The reason we create routines is to help our children order their worlds. We all crave routine. You are not a slave to the routine. It is your servant, not your master.

How can we do it?

Create a master weekly schedule. Weekly routines inject fun into your week. Maybe Friday afternoon is beach day. Or Tuesday morning is story time at the library. Or one morning a week is a play date. Just like us, your children love knowing what is coming in the future and looking forward to it.

You can download a weekly form and read more on this topic here **thedisciplemakingparent.com/suggestions-for-creating-structure-in-an-unstructured-week/**. The purpose of this schedule is NOT to make you a slave to it. It is to give order.

Create a master daily schedule. While the weekly schedule works for big picture items, a daily schedule is helpful when you are juggling multiple children. What will your three-year-old be doing while you are feeding your three-month-old? When your six-year-old is reading, what will your three-year-old be doing?

Creating a daily routine allowed us to prethink about rewards. For our children, enduring long New England winter days, Zoboomafoo on PBS at 5 pm was a great reward. They loved it and it allowed Sharon to cook dinner. Used prudently, screen time can be a great help.

Activities You Can Do

The following section has a list of different activities that you may put in your week.

Individual Book Time
We wanted to inculcate a love of books and a love of reading. The best way to do this is by surrounding them with good books all of their lives.

We started with book time because they can look at books before they can read. Many mornings, before we were even awake, we would stumble into the room of the bouncing toddler, toss some books to them, and stumble back to our bed to wake up. Older children who were out of their crib also had a set of books right by their bed. They could reach down and grab them without us even getting out of bed.

Individual Reading Time
When your children can read, this becomes a part of their day. Whether the early morning reading or looking at board books, this time is set aside for a little more difficult reading.

Family Reading Time
This was often the favorite time of the day for everyone. Mom reads a book while the children snuggle around on the couch. This activity fires the children's imagination, binds the hearts together, and gives the children a love of literature.

High-chair time
Perfect for right after a meal. Use cars, play-dough, or coloring to occupy the hands of the child who is contented from food. This time for young children links nicely with table time for older children.

Table time
Right after breakfast while the children were still fresh. We would often put on a teaching tape (now CD now mp3, now streaming), like *Adventures in Odyssey* or other *Focus on the Family Radio Theater*. Older children could draw, color, or play cars. And, of course, these materials were right by the table to allow easy access or self-service. This time allowed Mom to clean up breakfast dishes or a little breathing time before officially beginning the day.

Pack-n-Play Time
Pack-n-play time begins while your child is still in the car seat. Lay them on their back and put something like a baby gym. Come and get them before they fuss, or after they calm down. Don't train them that fussing gets them out. This eventually turns

into room time (see below) with a gate in the door so that you are still in control of the routine.

 For more information on pack-n-play time listen to
The Disciple-Making Parent Podcast Episode 20: A Baby's First Year.

Room Time

Room time is the natural graduation from pack-n-play time. We would put a gate up in the room, pull out a few toys like Duplos, Legos, Hot Wheels cars, or playing with little animals. Every child needs some quiet time to play by themselves. It calms them down and teaches them to focus.

Cleanup Time

Most "times" end with cleanup time. Toys or craft material is put in its place. Dishes are cleaned up from the meal. Think of it as the ending point of every activity. You get things out to play with. Assuming you are done with the project, you put them away.

You don't have to be super strict. If a project is ongoing then by all means leave the toys out. The goal is to keep the house from creating mess after mess that only gets cleaned up in the afternoon (if at all).

Outside Time

How good fresh air is! Outside time can be time Mom kicks the kids out of the house to be creative outside. If the neighborhood is safe, they can be expected to find something to do. If not, then the parents need to provide something to do like a trampoline or basketball hoop. Children definitely need to get their energy out. Our children would play basketball, jump on the trampoline, play circus, climb trees, ride scooters on the driveway. We parented by offering ideas and unstructured play. And it gave Sharon and I great joy to see them play "circus" and create games on the trampoline.

Creative Play Together

A variation of outside playtime, playing together as a family creates all sorts of training opportunities. Since our children were two years apart, they had great fun playing as they grew older.

During some of the long winters in New England, we might send them to the basement to play dress-up or up to their room to play "zoo" with their animals. Playing together is different than individual room time. While individual room time gives the introvert a chance to play by himself, playing together gives a chance to build family unity. Parents should often give some coaching at the beginning of the time and debrief at the end of the time. In addition, they should be ready to interrupt what they are doing to coach through the inevitable conflicts that will happen.

Dad and Mom remember: Conflict will happen during this time. It is your chance to coach them in loving, sharing, sacrificing, asking questions, not bossing, etc. If you assume you will not be interrupted, you are going to become angry.

Screen Time
Should be used discerningly but still very helpful. Can be educational videos or fun videos. Can be used as a reward right before lunch or dinner.

Video Time
This time should be used carefully, but it is helpful.

There are some great shows on PBS or on DVDs that you choose. We all need some distraction when we are tired at the end of the day. I grew up on Mister Rogers. My kids grew up on Zoboomafoo.

As parents, we were probably a little overly concerned about creating children with ADD or lacking creativity from too much screen time. Nevertheless, it was great to have a reward and a "babysitter" in the late afternoon hours when everyone was tired, hungry, and Mom was trying to get dinner prepared. Plus, when the kids are mesmerized by the TV and hungry, they don't realize how many carrot sticks you are feeding them!

Chore Time
It is good for each child to have chores around the house. It is also encouraging and motivating to work as each one is working. Chore time is a part of the day where everyone is working on chores that cleanup the house. Or it may also be a time of the week like Saturday mornings.

A chart is helpful here so that every child knows what is expected. But once every child knows what is expected, it is motivating to know that it is "chore time." As a parent balance the need to get the chore done with the need to train your children to do chores. Training takes more time in the short term but brings long term fruit.

Five Reasons a Timer is Your Friend

In this section, I want to persuade of timers in your parenting. While timers seem like a cold and sterile way to organize your house, they are actually helpful.

Sharon and I had them scattered all over the house. We had one in each bedroom, one in the kitchen, one in the den, one on top of the piano (for practice) and one next to the dreaded blue chair where they had to sit at times for discipline.

Obviously, we did not use all of them at the same time. Rarely did we have more than one going, but having them in all the rooms prevented us from having to search for a timer.

First, it minimizes fussing, arguments, and discussion. Timers serve as an outside authority. When you say, "We are going to have room time for 30 minutes," an external authority has been set. The play-time is not arbitrary. It is not until they fuss or get tired. It is not up for grabs.

Second, it creates healthy boundaries in the children. Once the timer is set, they cannot think about all the things they could be doing. They need to focus on one activity right now. They know that Mom or Dad is not going to give in and relent. If they fuss or complain, the time will just be extended.

Third, it creates confidence in the children. This activity is not going to go on forever. If they don't enjoy what they are doing, they know it will not go on forever. If they don't enjoy looking at books, then they only have to look at them for 30 minutes. If they don't enjoy being outside, then they will only have to survive the cold for an hour. There is an end in sight.

Fourth, it frees the parent to go do something else. How many parents have said, "I don't even have time to make a phone call or go to the bathroom. My children follow me around all day."

Part of our job as a parent is to make our children independent of us. Loving them does not mean making them dependent on us. They are a welcome addition to our world but not the center. When you became a parent, you did not cease to be: a child of God, a spouse, a friend, a church member.

Timers give you boundaries that encourage their independent play and give you time to go about your own God-given responsibilities.

Fifth, it reminds the parent to move on to the next activity. Setting the timer doesn't mean you have to end the activity. But it can remind you. You want to communicate to your children that you are the authority. You decide what you are doing during the day. Moving on to different activities happens because you are a wise parent NOT because they start fussing.

Also, while some parents hover and need to be reminded to back off, other parents can become so involved in another activity that they lose track of time. Sharon would often take some free time to encourage or counsel a woman in our church. But because those conversations could be quite long, the children's timer reminded her about other goals she had for the day.

Unobtrusive but Helpful
Obviously there is much more to our parenting than setting timers throughout our day. If you were in our home, you might have noticed them as an unobtrusive part of the daily routine. Nonetheless, they were an essential way of encouraging the order of the day and the self-government of the children.

Conclusion
We all crave routines and order. We have this order not in an oppressive way but in a gracious way. God's gracious routines of daily sunlight and yearly seasons creates joy not oppression. A well-ordered family results in happier children and happier parents.

Understanding Correction, Consequences, Chastisement, and Rewards

LECTURE NOTES

Parents, Use Correction, Consequences, Chastisement, and Rewards

Scriptural Basis for Disciplining Our Children

- We discipline, bringing negative consequences to our children, because the Father does this to us. We are imitating him – the most loving Father there is!
- We understand how to relate to our child by looking at how our Father relates to us.
- We discipline as standing in the Lord's place – as his undershepherds.

We don't understand -

> God's goodness and his use of pain
> to help us grow
> are not
> contradictory or mutually exclusive."

Hebrews 12:5-11.

> *"My son, do not regard lightly the discipline of the Lord,*
> *nor be weary when reproved by him.*
> *⁶ For the Lord disciplines the one he loves,*
> *and chastises every son whom he receives."*

> ⁷ It is for discipline that you have to endure. God is treating you as sons. For what son is there whom his father does not discipline? ⁸ If you are left without discipline, in which all have participated, then you are illegitimate children and not sons. ⁹ Besides this, we have had earthly fathers who disciplined us and we respected them. Shall we not much more be subject to the Father of spirits and live? ¹⁰ For they disciplined us for a short time as it seemed best to them, but he disciplines us for our good, that we may share his holiness. ¹¹ For the moment all discipline seems painful rather than pleasant, but but later it yields the peaceful fruit of righteousness to those who have been trained by it.

Principles from this passage.

1. Discipline is from God. (v.6) **-** The Lord disciplines. We are like him when we discipline.

2. Discipline is an act of _____ . (v.6) - God is love, and yet he disciplines us *because* he loves. To not discipline is to hate. The motive is love.

3. Discipline starts with fathers. (v.7) - Fathers should take the lead in disciplining.

4. Discipline results in respect toward parents. (v.9) - Proper discipline results in respect not alienation.

5. Discipline is for a _____ time. (v.10) - Believe it or not, you will not always be correcting them.

6. Discipline is imperfect. (v.10) - *As they thought best*. We will not discipline perfectly. They will survive. We should not hold back out of fear of "messing up" our child.

7. Discipline is painful. (v. 11) – The pain of the discipline should be more than the pleasure of disobedience. It is hard to inflict negative consequences on our children, but it is necessary.

8. Discipline results in righteousness/_____ . (v.11) – It yields peace and righteousness later. Peace in the home. Peace in the heart. Righteousness in the soul.

9. Discipline has a purpose. (v.10) - To train in holiness.

10. Discipline is heart oriented. (vv. 5, 11) – This might surprise you but the writer aims comments at the heart of the disciplined. One can accept discipline or one can become embittered and not learn from discipline.

Proverbs on Discipline

- *Whoever spares the rod hates his son, but he who loves him is diligent to discipline him (13:24).*
- *Discipline your son, for there is hope; do not set your heart on putting him to death (19:18).*
- *Discipline your son, and he will give you rest; he will give delight to your heart (29:17).*
- *Do not withhold discipline from a child, if you strike him with a rod, he will not die. If you strike him with the rod, you will save his soul from Sheol (23:13-14).*

Isolation vs. Time Out
- Isolation is helpful for social sins. But it is a consequence for a purpose. Time-out is simply a punishment or consequence given without a purpose.
- An example of isolation with a purpose is, "Go on the blue chair until you can come up with 3 things about your brother that you are thankful for."
- Isolation is helpful before/after discipline – "Take some time to get yourself under control and then I will come back to talk and pray with you."

Examples of Consequences Besides Chastisement
- Complaining – "Go sit on the blue chair for two minutes. Ask the Lord to help you. And then come back with three thankful things."
- Temper tantrum - Isolation in room, then chastisement.
- "Tired" in church – Donuts are a natural privilege after church. No refreshments after church if you are tired.
- Getting out of bed after being put to bed – After putting to bed, give a privilege that can be removed. For example, give music or a story at night that soothes or distracts. It can be taken away for getting out of bed.
- Not eating food - Put food away and that bring it out again at the next meal. (We did have some exceptions.)
- Potty mouth – clean the potty.
- Physical – pushups, running around outside.
- Fussing about a chore – An extra chore.
- General social rudeness at dinner - Reward for good behavior. Isolation for negative.

A Few More Thoughts
- As parents, we are "coaches," not merely cheerleaders. Although we are our children's biggest fans, we don't just cheer. We also need to have actions with consequences. We do correct.
- If you do not train your child to submit to you, you are training them to disobey. As they get older they will resist good authority and it will not go well with them.

Parents, Prayerfully Consider Using Chastisement

Occasion and Benefits

*The word "spanking" has too often been used for child abuse such as slapping, punching, grabbing. Therefore, we will not use that word. We will use the biblical word **chastise**.*

What Do We Use Chastisement For?

1. Disobedience to your direct command
2. _____
3. Dishonesty
4. Other "serious" sins if other corrections are not working

Benefits

- Will not be remembered by children who are young.
- Instructs the conscience.
- Helps the child hit reset.
- Consequence is over quickly.
- Trains the child in obedience.
- Teaches your child to live under your authority.

Some Objections Answered

- Society says a child learns violence and it will harm the child's self-esteem.
- Unbiased sociological studies have shown this is not true.
- The reason most parents don't chastise is because of the pain the parents feel, because of their experience as children, or not trusting God's word.

10 Steps for Applying Chastisement

1. Don't chastise when you are _____. If you are angry, isolate them until you are under control. See the essay, *Parents, Know How to Overcome Your Anger*.
2. Always chastise alone, never in public. At home and in private.
3. Make sure to include confession and instruction. "What did you do wrong?" Make sure they know what they did wrong.
4. Assure them you are doing this out of love. "I am not disciplining you because I am angry but because God tells me to do this to train your heart."
5. Apply proper discipline. On the bottom, with an implement, appropriate to the offense.
6. Give a break to regain his composure. Sometimes a time break is helpful here.
7. _____ together. "Let's pray and ask the Lord to forgive you for (the sin). And let's ask Him to help you do (the positive) next time."
8. He/She prays. Confessing the sin to put off and the virtue to put on.

9. You pray. Thanking God for him/her, this lesson, the blood of Christ, and the power to change.
10. Give affirmation. Hugs. Affirmation. Upbeat. "Now let's go have a good day."

See the short essays on the following pages:
- *Dad, Take the Lead in Discipline, Mom, Do Your Part*
- *Parents, Hand out Consequences Consistently*
- *Parents, Know How to Handle Disagreements Among Yourselves*
- *Parents, Think about How to Handle Grandparents Who Disagree with You*
- *Parents, Know How to Overcome Your Anger*

Parents, Understand Miscellaneous Principles for Obedience

1. Child training is a misnomer. It is actually _____ training. Consistency is vital.

2. Every disobedience should command your attention whether you actually do something about it right then or not.

3. _____ should take the lead in this area. When Dad is home, he does the discipline. Dad - do not be lazy. You are coming home to your real job. See the essay, *Dads, Take the Lead in Discipline. Moms Do Your Part.*

4. Win the battle at _____, not in public. Work hard at home. Better to wait to gain obedience at home than to correct in public. Home is training ground. Public is testing ground.

5. Realize issues often reappear when there is physical growth.

6. We disciplined for an offense of "Testing the limits."

7. At the in-laws, let the "home parent" correct. If you discipline, let it be the child of the parents whose house you are in. Don't worry about grandparents spoiling. Just pick up the pieces later. See the two essays, *Parents, Think About How to Handle Grandparents Who Disagree with You.*

8. Don't take pride in your parenting. Don't be embarrassed by your child. You are working for the King.

9. We are not responsible for acts of misbehavior. We are responsible for actions that characterize our children.

10. Get the _____. The others will follow.

11. Everything does not have to be a huge battle. Choose your battles wisely.

12. Ask, "What is going on behind the behavior?" Be sure to take time to consider this.

13. Don't discipline until you think it through and talk it through. For example, in anger parents say, "You are grounded for life." See the essay, *Parents, Hand Out Consequences Consistently.*

Parents, Think About The Rewards

Don't Give Away the "Ice Cream."

What rewards can you give them to motivate for distasteful tasks?
- "Clean up your toys and then we can go play with friends."
- "Finish your dinner and you can have dessert."
- "If everyone is in the car on time for church, we will stop for donuts.

Give Away the "Ice Cream."

What reward can you give them that you will take away if there is not good behavior?

- We let our children listen to tapes in bed provided they did not get out of bed.
- Screen time can be a great reward.
- The key is that you have to be ready and OK with taking it away.

Final Thoughts on Discipline

Parents, Consistency is Vital. Be Consistent Even When You Don't Feel Like It

- Kids are gamblers. It they think you will not follow through, they will take a chance.
- We have to be consistent as parents even when we are tired or it is inconvenient.

Parents, Realize That, Out of Love, God Trains Us with Things that are Unpleasant

- "Those whom I love, I rebuke and discipline" (Revelation 3:19).
- We are coaches, not just cheerleaders.

Parents, Parent by Faith Not Fear

- Actively trusting that God knows best in his Word.

NOTES

REFLECTION QUESTIONS

Use the following questions to guide your discussion.

1. How were you disciplined as a child? Does that affect your view of how to discipline?

2. How does understanding our Heavenly Father's discipline help you?

3. Are you using isolation constructively?

4. Do you have clear boundaries for what deserves chastisement?

5. Are you relying on chastisement too much or too little? Should you be using rewards more? Look back at your character chart to see which you are emphasizing.

ESSAYS

Parents, Understand an Abbreviated Plan for Child-Rearing

Many years ago, I came across a recording by a Christian pastor – Bill Goode. I loved it so much I wrote it down. The following are some of my notes that I think will be helpful. The first two sentences were his motto and the rest of the essay explains them.

"We praise a lot, we pray a lot, we play a lot, we teach a lot, and we use cause and effect a lot. And when we do spank, we do it lovingly, slowly and thoughtfully."

Praise a lot
Children who are praised a lot can tell the difference between right and wrong; what you do want and what you don't want. Jesus corrected Peter but he also praised Peter (Matt 16:17). The child who is only corrected has a hard time telling the difference between what you want and what you don't want, what's right and what's wrong.

Bring them up (Eph 6:4). Praise helps bring them up. Parents need to sit down separately and come up with strengths and weaknesses for each child. You need to praise him for those strengths. Then pick one weakness to work on over time (2-3 weeks).   A good coach comes alongside and helps the team whip the common enemy. Separate the problem from the person. Then say to him, "We're all going to gang up on this problem – the habit."

Play a lot
A merry heart does good like a medicine (Prov 17:22). Would your children say, "Our parents are fun to live with?" Life can be tough. We need to have fun. We need to ask ourselves, what kind of person am I? What kind of partner am I? What kind of parent am I?   Children need to learn the difference between work and play – fun and getting serious.

Pray a lot
Count it pure joy whenever you face trials of many kinds. (Jam 1:2) Trials are good. Even trials from our children. They drive us as parents to the grace of God. They drive us to the Word of God.

Teach a lot
Teaching is putting into the mind. In the story of Abraham & Isaac. Abraham must have taught Isaac this because of his willingness at the age of 12 to climb onto the altar to be sacrificed. Do not be timid about teaching children to honor parents -- that your days may be long.

Parents of older children (8 & up), you have to get to the mind of the child. You may have done a good job up to that point but fail to make that shift. The key is getting to the child's mind using the Proverbs. Bring them up with teaching. The Book of

Proverbs tells what a child can do. A child can learn. A child can choose his friends. Scripture memory is good. It puts Scripture into the mind and then associates with life experiences to get them thinking.

Use cause and effect a lot

You reap what you sow. (Gal 6:7). The most natural way of discipline is cause and effect. When we do chastise, we do so lovingly, slowly, prayerfully and thoughtfully. *Vengeance is mine says the Lord* (Rom 12:19). We don't get even with our child – we correct. One is selfish discipline and the other is discipline with a goal.

Trust completely your all-wise, loving, heavenly Father in your parenting. You can't push the buttons and have children come out perfectly. Proverbs says a child has an independent will and can choose good or evil. "Train up a child in the way he should go and when he is old, he will not depart from it" is a general truth, but there will be some children who will test us. We need to grow in being God's kind of person, God's kind of partner, and God's kind of parent no matter what happens.

Dad, Take the Lead in Discipline. Mom, Do Your Part

I was recently presenting at a conference and was suggesting that Aaron's son's sins of active disobedience and passive disobedience might have been influenced by Aaron's passivity as a leader. Though parents are certainly not responsible for the choices our children make as adults, we do have some influence over them as we shape their wills growing up.

One application of that talk was to strongly suggest that men fight passivity and engage in leading their home, especially in the area of child discipline.

At the end of that talk, one mom asked this question, "I have just come from a talk where the female speaker was urging the women not to be pushovers and put the discipline on the fathers. How would you fit those two thoughts together?"

This was a helpful question because it allowed me to correct what listeners might be hearing that I was not saying. My response was this:

I don't think we are contradicting each other at all. Men can have a temptation to be overbearing or passive in parenting. By far the most common struggle is passivity. Moms have temptations as well not to be the "bad guy" and inflict some sort of painful discipline on the little one that they love. They can be tempted to either spoil them or pass the buck to the father saying, "Just wait until your dad gets home." As a result, dads regularly walk into a messy situation at the end of the day and are too often the bad guy in the relationship.

Ideally, Mom and Dad are on the same page in terms of correction. Mom carries it out when Dad is not around. She only defers the "big things" to him. Dad makes sure that the family has a plan and the children are under control.

My wife and I tried to follow these principles.
1. Dad and Mom are a team in leading the household in the area of discipline with Dad ultimately responsible before God.

2. God expects and commands men to discipline their children (Ephesians 6:4, Hebrews 12:9, 1 Tim 3:4-5). When children are wild and disobedient it is a black mark on the man (Titus 1:6, 1 Tim 3:4-5).

3. Therefore, I as the dad, need to learn about parenting principles and make sure my wife and I are on the same page. As a dad, I can delegate but I cannot abdicate.

4. This means that we will learn together godly principles of child-rearing.

5. I will trust her as the person onsite the most with the children. She will be most in tune with what they need.

6. We will communicate often to come up with plans that are working and that she can implement. Dad will value Mom's insight and suggestions. Since Dad is to lead the family, Mom will bring issues to him and thoughtfully engage with his insights.

7. Since we are a team, we will not disagree about discipline in front of the children. We may have those disagreements offline. But in the moment, the children will see a united front.

8. Moms can and should correct and enforce the principles of discipline. Those same commands in #2, apply to women as co-regents with your husband.

9. When Dad is home, he will take the lead if discipline or correction needs to occur. He will not sit passively in the other room while his wife hands out discipline. This grows even truer the older the children become.

10. Moms will watch carefully their own temptation to overrule and disregard their husbands as well as passively pass all the difficult issues to him.

Conclusion
Mom and Dad together are a great team. Together they bring complementary insight. But Dads, we are responsible in this area to take the lead. So don't be lazy. God called you to this. You can do it!

Parents, Hand Out Consequences Consistently

A short parable that might be helpful to young parents.

A Parable of Two Police Officers
There once was a boy and a girl who grew up in a small town. As these stories go, Jonathan and Amy fell in love with each other and were married. But along the way they discovered something else they had in common – both loved their little town and they loved serving it.

n particular, Jonathan and Amy both loved keeping the peace and safety by being police officers. And so this husband and wife became officers of the law. And the community loved them. Two of their own would be serving the town!

Problems Arise
However, Jonathan and Amy soon realized that one particular aspect of their job was especially challenging. They had to give out speeding tickets. What made this a challenge was that, since they grew up in this town, they were giving the tickets out to their friends and people they loved.

At first they would just give their friends a warning. But they discovered that they were giving them lots of warnings. Their friends never seemed to change. Then they found their own hearts getting upset that they had to stop so many people. They would come home from work frustrated that their friends were not heeding their warning. They kept speeding!

What were they going to do? They felt like the joy was being sucked out of their job. Finally, they decided to have breakfast with Frank, the retired policeman who had served the city for many years. They would ask his advice.

After explaining the situation to them, Frank sympathized a little bit and then said, "The solution is fairly simple. The question is, 'Will you take my advice and be consistent with it?'"

"Yes," they said. "Anything. We love our jobs and the people. We are desperate."

An Old-Timer's Advice
Frank continued with things they must do.

First, you must believe in the laws. Run for city council so you can change the silly speed limits. Make sure all the speed limits are realistic and an expression of love. Also make sure the fines are real deterrents. A $20 ticket will probably not stop the behavior.

Second, every day get ready for work knowing that part of your job will be to give people you love speeding tickets. They will plead with you and tell you they don't have the money. You will feel torn in your heart. But if they are speeding, you must enforce the law. Remember it is act of love for their good. They don't realize how these laws will save their lives and the lives of others.

Third, give out your tickets with care and without anger. You can even sympathize with them. "Oh, Mrs. Jones are you speeding through this area again? Didn't I just give you a ticket last week? Well, this time the fine has to be doubled. I hope that will help you remember next time. I am doing this because I care."

"It was that simple?" thought Jonathan and Amy. "That was it?"

Jonathan and Amy had believed they were loving their friends by not giving tickets. Now they saw that loving their friends meant they *had* to give their friends tickets.

A Young Couple's New Perspective
And that's what the couple did.

First, they served on the city council so that all the speed limit laws were for people's real safety. There were no speed traps. They wanted their friends to have the maximum freedom and still have a safe, orderly community. But they also upped several fine amounts to be more effective.

Second, every day as they got ready to go to work, they knew they would encounter their friends speeding. They also knew they would be tempted to let them off with a warning. But they knew from past experience that only a real consequence would change behavior.

Third, because they went to work expecting their friends to speed, they found that they were less angry. They gave out tickets not because they were angry but with a little tinge of sadness.

Guess what happened to their little town? With better speed limits, better enforcement, and kinder police officers, the accidents in the town dropped dramatically. Jonathan and Amy found themselves better liked. The drivers knew they were breaking the law and deserved the consequence.

Jonathan and Amy were happier. Their friends (eventually) were happier. And the town was safer. All because of a change of perspective. By handing out consequences consistently and calmly, the town was more peaceful.

Parents of young children, go and do likewise.

Parents, Know How to Handle Parenting Disagreements Among Yourselves

What if my spouse and I disagree on child-rearing decision or philosophy?

This is a common question and a common occurrence. Two sinners will have different approaches to child-rearing, child discipline, and the individual decisions we each have to make for our children.

The following are six biblical suggestions to help you agree.

1. Value each other. Dads need the perspective of the mom and moms need the perspective of the dads. There usually is something valuable that each of us can hear in the concern of the other.

2. Realize the biblical call on both men and women to parent. Scripture says that elders (and thus all men) are to manage their own household well and see that their children obey him with all respect (1 Tim 3:4). And if the children are wild and disobedient it comes back to the dad (Titus 1:6). On the other hand, moms are God's intended primary disciple-makers and heart shapers. They are the ones onsite the most (Titus 2:3-4).

3. Fight the sinful temptations. The most common sinful temptation is for a man to give up his role as leader. That may be because he does not know what to do or because he feels his wife is an expert. And it is common for a wife to take control and subtly move her husband's leadership and influence to the side. Though he still plays with the kids, the tough parenting decisions and policy-making come from Mom. Moms, you need his input (see #1) and God sees him as the leader of the home (see #2). On the converse, you may be tempted to have the overbearing dad with the passive mom.

4. Seek out common child-rearing teaching together. It is vital that both husband and wife learn together and discuss together. This will allow them to make the decisions based on the same information. Learning together cannot be overrated. The sinful temptation for a passive father can begin because he has not received common teaching with his wife. She knows more than him and thus he feels inadequate.

5. Present a united front to your children. Try not to disagree in front of your children. Agree with the other parent's decision in front of the children. Then make a time to talk about it later.

6. Discern the size of the disagreements and take appropriate action. The Bible calls on a wife to yield to her husband's leadership and a husband to love his wife by seeking to understand her. How those commands are played out in life can be tricky. How are couples to handle disagreements?

The following suggestions are in order from small issues to big issues:

- **Drop it.** For small matters, maybe you should let it go. You can register your concern but given the myriad of decisions and the amount of time we have, some decisions we need to entrust to the other, usually the mom.

- **Talk about it behind closed doors.** We have already talked about this (in #5) but some immediate decisions may need to be talked about in private. You may need to decide to drop it for the moment and then discuss it later.

- **Talk about it later.** A coffee date night is a perfect chance to bring up bigger issues where there needs to be some time for each party to understand all the concerns of the other. In the busyness of life, you may have temporarily dropped it knowing that you needed a longer time to discuss an issue.

- **Pray about it together or separately.** Some big decisions where you are disagreeing will magically dissolve as you pray about it and ask the Lord for his promised wisdom.

- **Seek informal counsel.** Bounce questions off other wiser parents and pastors. Listen for things you may not be thinking about. Humility will cause us to ask for insight we might not be seeing.

- **Seek "binding arbitration."** On a few extremely important issues, there may be such a large disagreement that neither party thinks they can yield. In this case, it can be helpful to seek "binding arbitration." In 1 Corinthians 6 we are commanded to bring disputes to wise counselors for judgment. It can be helpful for a couple in a healthy church to agree to lay out their disagreement between one or two pastors and abide by their decisions.

Disagreements about parenting are inevitable. Disunity by the adults is not.

Parents, Think About How to Handle Grandparents Who Disagree with You

Question: We are Christians but both sets of our parents are not. How do we handle their disagreement with how we are raising our children (their grandchildren)?

I was recently asked that question at a conference. Thankfully, Sharon and I had wonderfully supportive parents. However, I have talked with enough families to begin to understand some of the problems. I know I risk giving simplistic answers to complex family situations and dynamics. Nevertheless, here is my reply.

We are commanded by God to honor our parents. Although we don't obey them as adults we are still called to honor. This plays out in several ways.

1. We should not speak evil of them in front of our children. We want to encourage honor for them in our children. Even if we must end up disagreeing or having frank conversations, we always want to present them in the best light possible to our children. In frustration, it may be easy to complain about them to our spouse with the children accidentally listening in.

2. Out of honor, seek to understand the concern they are expressing. Rather than just assume they don't have any wisdom because they are not Christians, assume they DO have some wisdom because they have lived longer. You don't have to follow everything they say because you listen to it. Try to dig underneath. Ask them, "What is it you are seeing that you think we don't see? What is your concern?"

3. In most cases, the biological child ought to speak with the grandparents in question. If there is a tense discussion to have, it can often defuse some of the tension by having the mother talk to her parents or the father talk to his parents. There are exceptions depending on the trust or lack of trust but in general this principle holds true.

4. Be willing to allow the grandparents to spoil in their house. That is the role of grandparents! It is their house so they can set the rules. My wife's grandfather used to say, "If you don't like the pancake you can throw it on the floor!" It will take work to undo some of that spoiling when you get home. That's ok. Being spoiled a little bit will not hurt your children.

5. On the other hand, we can't let grandparents undermine our authority. Unfortunately, I have heard of some situations where the grandparent essentially tells the children, "Well, your mom says we can't do this, but we are going to anyway." This is a wrong response by the grandparents. But if we, the parents, were a little less strict it might not put the grandparents in such an awkward position. Related to this, we want to secure the grandparents buy-in on a standard we might ask them to enforce.

6. There is one big exception to these last points – electronic access! We want to be extra vigilant about the electronic access our kids have at the grandparents' house. Do they have filters on their devices?

7. In addition, electronic devices as gifts might also be an exception. Similar to #6, while we may allow the grandparents to purchase gifts for the children at our house, I would strongly discourage them from purchasing electronics. We want it to be very clear that we the parents are providing use of electronics that belong to us. Therefore, we can limit access time, have passwords, and go on it anytime we want. After all it does not belong to the child but us. We are merely letting them borrow it for a moment.

No doubt there are an infinite number of scenarios based on family relationships and values. I offer these seven principles as a way forward.

Parents, Know How to Overcome Your Anger

Parenting with Patience is a 5-week, video-driven Bible study designed to help with this very issue. Visit ParentingwithPatienceStudy.com to learn more about this resource.

It is embarrassing, shame-inducing, and stress-relieving at the same time. It is rarely talked about or confessed in small groups. But it is prevalent in almost every home.

It's parental anger.

You may have thought of yourself as a patient person – until you started having children. Whether the constant physical demands of little ones, the continual testing of the middle ones, or the perplexing reactions of the teen, children can press us in new ways.

God has uniquely positioned children to shine a floodlight on the true state of our hearts. And at times, it is not pretty. We use words with an intensity that surprises and frightens us.

As a father of four young children and then, later, four teens, I remember thinking, "Wait. God commands *me* not to exasperate *them*? Shouldn't it be the other way around?"

But by God's grace, after searching the Scriptures in desperation to change, I found some help that allowed me to grow in patience. The following truths are meant to help parents with anger in a normal range. They are not intended for a more abusive situation. For that, seek out help from spiritual and legal authorities in your life.

What were those three key truths?

1. Understand What Anger Actually Is
Dr. David Powlison's definition has been helpful to me. Anger is "an active stance you take to oppose something you assess as important and wrong." Anger is active. It comes from our desires. It is a response to act against something that we believe is important and wrong.

This helps us understand one reason why God's anger is righteous and Jesus was angry with the Pharisees. He alone perfectly understands and defines what is important and wrong. It also explains why God commands his people, "In your anger, do not sin" (Eph 4:26). While some anger itself may not be specifically sinful, it is uniquely positioned to cause us to sin.

But if anger is not always sinful, Scripture is filled with commands that help us see how anger is usually filled with sin.

2. Understand Anger As Your Foe
Sinful anger is an enemy. Jesus taught us that sinful anger is miniature murder (Matt 5:21-22), grieves the Spirit (Eph 4:30), and is driven by the flesh (Gal 5:20). It will not fix the problem (James 1:20) and actually injures the other person (Prov 12:18). In

the words of Dr. Ed Welch, "To be angry is to destroy." My anger destroys the peace of my child, the trust of my child, and my testimony to her as a follower of Christ.

As a parent, it is so easy to justify my anger as righteous or move on quickly after a blow-up. But sinful anger truly is a deadly foe that I need to put to death by the Spirit.

But if that is our only thinking, we are setting ourselves up for failure. Because we are not understanding the whole of Scripture. It often takes two statements to provide a balanced view of what Scripture teaches.

3. Understand Anger as Your Friend
We also need to see that anger can be our friend. Wait! You just said anger is a foe. Yes, but if understood correctly, I can also see some anger as a friend. To reference our definition again, it is an indicator that something "is important and wrong." It is an emotion God has given us. But it is to be used to attack a problem not a person.

Godly parenting is not a placid, Zen-like trance. A father who watches his teen son talk back to his mother and has no reaction reveals a deficiency in him. The mother who is oblivious while her six-year-old hits a younger child is not honoring Christ.

Rather than blowing up in the moment, we need to let that anger motivate us to ask, "What problem is this pointing me to? What is important and wrong?"

Digging Deeper on Our Desires
Often we quote James 4:1-2 which tells us that fights come from our desires that battle within us. Rightly that verse helps us drill down to examine when our desires become idolatrous demands.

But not all of our desires are sinful. There are good desires we have as a parent. Our daughter should obey us. Our son should have done his homework. God calls parents to train and disciple their children. That means they need our correction at times. In fact, if we don't provide some consequences to the disobedient daughter or the lax son, we are negligent in our duties as a parent.

Perhaps, looking back at the angry moment, our desire did become a demand. But the desire itself is not the problem. As wise parents, we need to let that upset motivate us to come up with a solution to the problem.

In the 1990s, I was a programmer for a bank. In those days before the Internet (yes, the Internet did not always exist!), I might receive a call in the middle of the night about a problem. When that happened, I took two steps. One was to fix the problem so that the bank could open in the morning. But the second occurred the next morning. I would review what had happened and then come up with a solution that would prevent getting a call in the future. I assumed the problem would happen again and used this as a time to review the operations.

In a similar manner, assuming our desire is a good one like obedience or responsibility, the upset is an indicator that something needs to change -- in my heart, in my kids, or my home management. God calls all of us, men and women, to manage our households well. Anger is to be used to come up with a plan. Let the anger drive you to find solutions to the issue that is causing the upset.

Conclusion

The Lord and my children have graciously overlooked much sin on my part. Until Jesus returns, our home life will be messy. Mine certainly was. But we can and should make progress in becoming like Jesus. Our children are sanctification machines, providentially sent by God. We can grow in becoming more patient and better leaders in our homes by overcoming our anger.

For more help on this topic, visit: **ParentingwithPatienceStudy.com**

LESSON
7

Understanding
How to Get Started

LECTURE NOTES

Parents, Don't Be Discouraged.
Think About Getting Started

7 Steps to Get Started

1. Slow down and _____. Make a list of everything but...

2. Call the legislature into session. Pray for wisdom and priorities.

3. Work on a _____ things at a time, for a time. Put them on the character chart.

4. Talk to them individually. "Mom and Dad see the need to honor the Lord better in our family life. Here is something that is not pleasing him. Here is our plan."

5. _____ the consequences and rewards.

6. Attack the sin not the person. Work together to conquer the common enemy of the flesh and devil.

7. Follow through with consequences without anger. You are going to expect disobedience, so why are you angry? Train, retrain and discipline.

A Case Study: A Sample Letter for an Arguing Young Child

Dear Chap,

Can you help me with my almost 5-year-old daughter? She regularly complains and challenges anything we tell her to do. The pressing issue of this moment is that she does not wait for us at breakfast but serves herself cereal.

Thanks, James

Dear James,

It has taken you time to get into this situation and it will take you time to get out of it but you can.

1. Treat complaining seriously as disobedience, as an offense against you and God.

2. Parents can train for obedience. We can train them to obey us, "all the way, right away, and in a happy way," was what Sharon and I used to say. They are capable. Do you believe it?

3. Create "formative discipline" house rules or habits that decrease the conflict. Routines that we always do that prevent many immediate battles. "What is our family's rule about breakfast?" Everything shouud not be up for grabs.

4. Create margin in your schedule to discipline. Child training is the highest goal, not getting your list accomplished.

5. Talk with your wife to get on the same page. Set up a consequence chart. I think it should include chastisement. It is helpful in the moment to refer to the established plan.

6. Make training your daughter a "project" or "campaign."

- with explanation to your daughter including Bible verses.
- with a *put off* and *put on* and use the character chart to remind her.
- bringing the gospel in.
- with role playing the right way to accept a "no" from you or your wife.
- with warning about coming consequences.
- with negative consequences after lots of training and perhaps with rewards.
- with lots of praise when she does not complain.
- with your arm around her literally or figuratively. She is not the problem. The quarreling is. You and she are going to attack this problem.

Institute an appeal process when she is allowed to give you more information. "Please may I appeal, Dad?" "What new information are you going to give me?"

Concluding Thoughts

Remember:

_____ at making disciples of Jesus Christ.

_____. And keep constantly correcting.

Seek to be faithful. They come messed up.

Seek to be humble.

Dads, stay involved.

Practice authority and affection.

NOTES

NOTES

REFLECTION QUESTIONS

Use the following questions to guide your discussion.

1. As you think back over the study, what new, biblical ideas challenged you most deeply?

2. Based on all that you have learned, how has your perspective changed on parenting? Do you feel more confident in your parenting now that you know God's word?

3. What do you plan to put into practice from this study immediately?

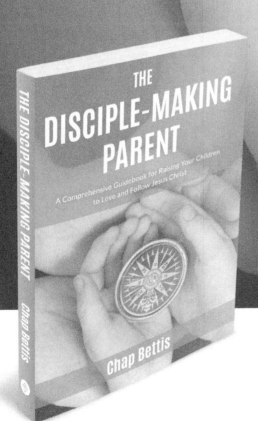

Ashamed of your yelling?

Parenting with Patience will you overcome your anger!

For more information or to order in bulk visit **parentingwithpatience.com**

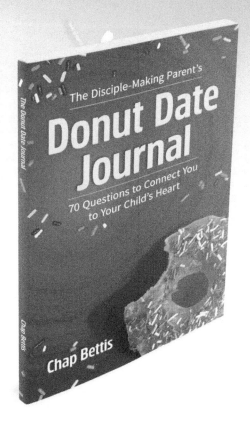

Made in the USA
Middletown, DE
26 January 2023

21828990R00077